A GUIDE TO THE INDUSTRIAL HISTORY OF GUILDFORD
AND ITS BOROⁱⁱᵍ
BY FRANCIS HA

G000089625

53: Guildford Town Mill

Reproduced by courtesy of Guildford Museum

INTRODUCTION

GUILFORD, an antient town of Surry, noted formerly for its manufactory of cloth, of which there are still some small remains. It has a number of good inns, with excellent accommodations, being a great thoroughfare on the road from London to Portsmouth....... It is seated on a declivity of a hill on the river Wey which is navigable to the Thames and by which a great quantity of timber is carried to London, not only from the neighbourhood but from Sussex and Hampshire woods above 30 miles off. Market (chiefly for corn) on Saturday.
from *A Complete and Universal Dictionary of the English Language* by the Reverend James Barclay. 1812.

The area covered by this book can be defined as not only the town of Guildford itself but also the outlying territory covered by the Borough of Guildford. As well as the usual lists of remains and sites, I have also included two longer articles which draw attention to special aspects of the Guildford area's industrial history.
Francis Haveron

WARNING
MANY OF THE SITES LISTED ARE ON PRIVATE PROPERTY AND PERMISSION TO VIEW MUST BE SOUGHT FROM THE OWNERS. NOTE ALSO THAT THE DESCRIPTIONS AND USES OF THE BUILDINGS, SITES OR OBJECTS ARE THOSE WHEN LAST VISITED BY THE COMPILER OF THE BOOK OR SUPPLIER OF THE INFORMATION

The so-called 'Pilgrim's Way' along the chalk ridge of the North Downs has probably little to do with pilgrims despite a story made popular in the 19th century. It provided a pre-historic route from the Kent coast to Salisbury Plain and traces of Mesolithic, Bronze Age, Iron Age and Saxon peoples have been found along and around it. There was a parallel track along the sand outcropping further down the hill slopes.

As a town built around a gap in the Downs and a ford across the river, Guildford became a focus for roads going from London to the south. The town's growth was accelerated by the rise of Portsmouth as a major naval base and the increase in coaching. Travellers found it convenient to change horses here or rest overnight. The road from Kingston to Sheetbridge near Petersfield was turnpiked in 1749, the road to Arundel in 1757, followed in 1758 by the Leatherhead road and the Farnham road over the Hog's Back. It should be noted that two 'Toll House Cottages' at Merrow (**TQ 024 505**) and on the Shalford Road (**TQ 999 483**) are not original tollhouses but were built on the site of previous ones. Other Guildford tollgates were sited on the Portsmouth road near the entrance to Guildown (**SU 994 486**) and on the summit of the Farnham road ascent (**SU 968 487**). A building which calls itself a tollhouse opposite the Squirrel Inn at Hurtmore (**SU 948 452**) on the modern Godalming to Farnham road seems to have no justification for the name.

The Wey Navigation was built at the instigation of Sir Richard Weston who had seen the canals of Holland during his exile in the Civil War. He had built a lock at Stoke in the 1620s and improved a stretch of river on his land as an experiment in irrigation. The canal was opened to Guildford in 1653 and 'has a good claim to be considered the first instance in England of a river made navigable by locks.' (Malden, 1900). Cargoes of timber, coal, corn and beer were carried. An extension, the Godalming Navigation, was opened in 1763. By 1958 all commercial traffic had stopped and in 1964 the Wey Navigation was given to the National Trust by Harry Stevens; the Godalming Navigation was given in 1968 to Guildford Corporation who transferred it to the National Trust. The Basingstoke Canal opened from the Wey Navigation to Basingstoke in 1796. Commercial traffic to Basingstoke ceased in 1901 and to Woking in 1949. The Surrey and Hants Canal Society was formed in 1966 and in the 1970s their respective lengths of the Canal were purchased by the two Counties. Restoration was finished in 1991.

The Wey and Arun Junction Canal opened in 1816 but closed in 1871. It leaves the Godalming Navigation at Shalford and then heads for the River Arun near Billingshurst in Sussex. Although it carried timber and other goods, even bullion from Portsea, it never exceeded its first year tonnage of 3,500 tons. Despite the demolition of many locks in the Second World War, the Wey & Arun Canal Society (1970) and Trust (1973) have campaigned to re-open the Canal. Some features have been restored–at least seven bridges have been reconstructed and two locks rebuilt.

Many local firms still surviving today especially in Guildford developed with the growth of the motor vehicle industry which has also left its mark on the face of the town. A number of existing motor firms have their origins in the early days of the motor car, especially Puttock's of Guildford (1905), Warn's of Shalford (1908 and claiming to be one of the longest established family-run garage firms in the country), Coombes Garage of Portsmouth Road, Guildford, Safeguard bus company, Guildford (1924), Methold's of Ripley, (1934), and Court & Smith, now at Ripley but who started as repairers in Friary Street, Guildford, in the 1930s. An early purpose-built showroom for cars was No 274 Upper High St, Guildford, (originally Crow Bros), which has had many subsequent occupants but still retains its interesting facade.

The 'Guildford', a 1920 cycle car, was made by Griffiths Engineering Works, Guildford. The 'LMB', made by LMB Components Ltd of Weyford House, Woodbridge Meadows, Guildford, 1960-1962, made use of Ford parts and either Ford or BMC engines under a fibre-glass body. In the field of sports and racing cars, the area has produced the famous Connaught cars (Connaught Cars Ltd, Portsmouth Road, Send) between 1948 and 1954, the Tyrell Formula I Grand Prix cars at Ockham, which started in 1969 and which still continue. One can even claim the Ferrari Grand Prix cars

1 *Angel Hotel*, Guildford
Photo: Chris Shepheard

whose design headquarters has been based at Broadford Road, Shalford. Here Ferrari's Technical Office Ltd build the Formula I chassis and manufacture suspension parts.

In motor-cycle manufacture, a name of national importance used to be that of the Blackburne firm at Tongham. Cecil and Alick Burney started Burney and Blackburne in 1908; they were originally connected with De Havilland engines until they started making their own and later complete motorcycles. They left the company in 1921 when the making of their engines was taken over by the Osborn Engineering Co of Gosport. As early as 1904, A W Wall was making his ROC motorcycles in Guildford; he was always full of unorthodox ideas and seems to have been often ahead of his times. His early machines had long and low frames; by 1906 he was building machines with good 2-speed gears and clutches and he was one of the first to introduce 4-speed gearboxes in England. Later, he went on to make the Wall autowheel, numerous motorcycles and other designs.

As for the Guildford area's links with cycling history, see the article by Les Bowerman, page 34.

The original planned railway route to Guildford from Woking and London by the Guildford Junction Company intended to use Prosser's system of flangeless wheels run on flat wooden rails kept in position by additional guide wheels but the London and South Western Railway wisely insisted on a conventional railway. The line from London to Guildford was opened to public traffic in May 1845. The following year, the Guildford to Farnham line was authorised and the track as far as Ash Junction was opened on August 20, 1849. At the same time, the Guildford to Shalford part of the Guildford extension was opened, with tunnels under the Mount and St Catherine's Hill just beyond Guildford Station. Although Godalming was reached in 1849, the Portsmouth Direct Line, using a slightly realigned route and a new station at Godalming, was not constructed until ten years later. The Guildford to Horsham line opened in 1865 and the branch line to Surbiton and Waterloo via Cobham was opened in 1885.

In 1849, the London and South Western Railway opened a line from Guildford to Alton via Ash Junction to Ash Green and Tongham and thence to Farnham through Runfold. Tongham Station was near the Anchor Inn and the line became of great use when the Aldershot Camp was built. From 1854 to 1860, a light single track railway followed the line of Ash Road into Aldershot, culminating near the Farnborough Road. The South Eastern and Chatham Railway shared the LSWR rails through Guildford aspart of their line from Ashford to Reading.

A service of electrified trains from Waterloo to Guildford via Bookham, Effingham and Horsley first started in July 1925. Stations at Ash Green and Tongham were closed down following electrification in 1937 when trains were re-routed to the north. The Tongham line survived until 1961 to serve a gas works.

ROADS, INNS AND FORGES

1 GUILDFORD: *ANGEL HOTEL*

SU 997 495   **LSII** ✻

Angel Hotel coaching inn, High Street. One of the town's famous coaching inns, dating from before 1527. Elegant black and white exterior of 1820 concealing the Jacobean timber framing and still carrying the signs **POSTING HOUSE** and **LIVERY STABLES**. Coaching was killed by the coming of the railway; five coaches survived until 1849 but ceased then. Public outcry in 1990 influenced the Guildford Borough Council to save the building from development. Of the other famous inns of the High Street, the *Crown*, traditional headquarters of the Whig party, became a shop in the 1850s and is now the NatWest Bank with a replica of the old crown sign above the Bank's sign. The *White Hart*, once the Conservative party headquarters, was demolished in 1905 to build Sainsbury's and an engraved marble mural plaque to commemorate this history is by the entrance. The *White Lion* with radical political associations lasted until 1965 when it was demolished to build Woolworth's which in turn was replaced by White Lion Walk; a fibre-glass figure of a white lion cast from an original from the old inn can still be seen over one of the entrances.

2 GUILDFORD: *THE HORSE AND GROOM*

TQ 028 508   **LSII** ✻

Epsom Road, Merrow. Formerly an inn called *The Running Horse*. The building is dated 1615 and as an inn was associated with a once famous race course on Merrow Downs a quarter of a mile away which was started with the royal support of William III about 1700 and later of George I but declined in the early 19th century. Subsequently, the Guildford Golf Club, one of the pioneers of the game in the Home Counties, occupied the area from 1886.

3 GUILDFORD: THE MOUNT

SU 993 493   ✻

Course of old turnpike road (1759) from Guildford to Farnham along the chalk ridgeway of the Hog's Back. It was so steep, however, that extra horses had to be kept at the *Wheatsheaf Inn* at the bottom to help coaches up. The present Farnham Road was built in the late 1790s with an easier slope.

4 GUILDFORD: BYPASS

TQ 010 509   ✻

Guildford and Godalming Bypass road (originally part of the A3 London-Portsmouth road.) 1934. During the Depression years of the early 1930s, the people of Guildford resolved to 'beat the terrible congestion' of the High Street as well as helping the unemployed by finding work for them to do. As a result of the public subscribing over half a million pounds, a work force of about 400 people was employed in building the nine mile long Bypass, taking traffic away from Guildford and also from Godalming.

5 OCKHAM: OLD FORGE

TQ 077 568   ✻

Ockham Lane. Built in 1840 for the Lovelace Estate as forge and wheelwright's shop. Unused for 35 years but now an artist's studio.

6 RIPLEY: *THE TALBOT*

TQ 054 569   ✻

An inn associated with coaching and with cycling. First mentioned in 1580 but mostly a 17th century building with a Georgian front and coach arch. Allegedly a meeting place for Lord Nelson and Emma Hamilton. The only survivor of three inns. The *White Hart* is now a shop and the *St George* is a private house.

7 SHERE: OLD FORGE

TQ 072 478   ✻

Lower Street. A cottage converted from a 17th century wheelwright's forge. The house next door called 'Wheelwrights' has the old tyring platform preserved in its front garden. A blacksmith's forge in Middle Street dating from 1914, has a typical stable door and is occasionally used for blacksmithing work.

4 4: Guildford Bypass under construction

Tony Martin Collection

BRIDGES

8 BRAMLEY: GOSDEN COMMON BRIDGES
TQ 006 457 ✳

A 'roving bridge' over the Wey and Arun Canal is incorporated into a later bridge over the canal and the former Horsham to Guildford line (1865-1965) which is now followed by the Downs Link footpath. A former tanyard nearby is occupied by a light engineering works. A low four-arch aquaduct (TQ 006 456) takes the canal over the Bramley stream. The bridge and aquaduct have been restored by the Wey and Arun Trust and other voluntary help.

9 CHILWORTH: RAILWAY FOOTBRIDGE
TQ 031 473

The 129 year old railway footbridge which used to span the platforms at Chilworth Station was about to be broken up but was saved by David Shepherd and moved to his East Somerset Railway in 1978.

10 CHILWORTH: PACKHORSE BRIDGE
TQ 028 475 ■

On Chilworth gunpowder site.

11 EASHING: BRIDGES
SU 946 438   LSi SC NT ✳

Two medieval stone bridges over the River Wey, probably part of a series of bridges built in the 13th century by monks from the Cistercian abbey of Waverley near Farnham. The design is similar to the bridges built at Tilford (SU 872 435 and 874 434), Elstead (SU 905 438) and Unstead (SU 993 454). This last bridge has railings with iron caps embossed WILLIAMS:FOUNDRY:FILMER:GUILDFORD .

12 GUILDFORD: ONSLOW BRIDGE
SU 993 495 ✳

Wrought iron with ornate decorations, opened by the Countess of Onslow in 1882.

13 GUILDFORD: TOWN BRIDGE
SU 995 494 ✳

In 1900, heavy floods swept away the existing 700 year old bridge which probably had been built by the monks from Waverley Abbey and subsequently modified in 1763 for the opening of the Godalming Navigation. In 1901 began the construction of a new bridge, a single 70 ft span carried on six braced steel ribs designed by John Webster, a London civil engineer. This was opened in 1902 and carried all the London-Portsmouth traffic until the Bypass was built in 1934 and was eventually closed to vehicles in 1973. After corrosion was found in 1983, parts of it were rebuilt.

14 GOMSHALL: PACKHORSE BRIDGE
TQ 084 479 ✳

At former Gomshall Tannery. Claimed to be of medieval origin.

15 PEASMARSH: UNSTEAD BRIDGE
SU 991 455 ✳

Tilthams Corner Road. Claimed to be of medieval origin.

16 SHALFORD: BRIDGE
SU 998 479 ✳

Shalford Road, over the Tillingbourne stream, dated 1758. Another similar bridge on the same stream 150 yards away to the west has a very low arch for carriages to cross on the level up the drive to the old Shalford House, now demolished.

17 SHERE: BRIDGE
TQ 074 478 ✳

Bridge over the Tillingbourne.

LOVELACE BRIDGES. There are only seven 'Lovelace' bridges in the Ockham-East Horsley area remaining out of the 24 made of flint and brick to the design of Lord Lovelace of Ockham in the mid-19th century. (See page 32; William King). Most are in very good condition after recent maintenance work by the Forestry Commission.

18 Dorking arch, Dorking Road.(TQ 100 512)

19 Raven arch, Greendene. (TQ 096 511)

20 Briary Hill, west, Scotch Plantation. (TQ 098 509)

21 Briary Hill, east, Scotch Plantation. (TQ 098 509)

22 Troy, Sheepwalk Lane. (TQ 096 502)

23 Hermitage, Sheepwalk Lane. (TQ 102 502)

24 Stoneydene, Stoneydene Plantation. (TQ 105 522)   All above, 18-24: ✳

CANALS

25 ASH VALE: CANAL WHARF
SU 894 534 ✳

Boatyard. Great Bottom Flash and embankment dates from 1794. Barges of the Basingstoke Canal were built and repaired here, the last in 1946. Originally the Wharf occupied some 3 acres of ground. The Ash Vale boathouse and barge building shed were established in stages from 1894 until 1947.

27: Dapdune Wharf, Guildford
Photo: Chris Shepheard

Barges and narrow boats were pulled out and repaired on the heathland opposite the boathouse from 1900 to 1948, the trees being used for anchors for the winches. Two canal-owned sand and gravel pits are visible near Mytchett Lake (**SU 892 542**). The last barge to reach Basingstoke took 15 tons of moulding sand from this site to Willis and Stevens engineers in Basingstoke in 1901; other locations were supplied until 1916.

26 GUILDFORD: TREADWHEEL CRANE

SU 994 494 *see cover drawing*　**LSII* SC NT ✳**

The treadwheel operated crane, at Guildford Wharf, is one of the most important industrial archaeological relics in Surrey. It probably dates from the earliest days of the Wey Navigation which opened in 1653 although there was no wharf at Guildford for the first ten years. The existing accounts dating from 1726 show annual purchases of new ropes for the crane. The 18ft diameter treadwheel was operated by local man or boy power, though convicts or donkeys have also been suggested. Not many of the timbers are original. In 1908 it ceased operation and in 1971 it was renovated by Guildford Borough Council for the National Trust. Similar cranes used to be at Stonebridge Wharf, Shalford, and at Godalming Wharf.

27 GUILDFORD: DAPDUNE WHARF

SU 993 503　　　　　　**LSII NT ☐**

Off Wharf Lane. A boatbuilding and repair yard for the Wey Navigation, now restored. The graving dock, capstans, nail store, forge, a brickbuilt steam-chest for softening planks and the master carpenter's cottage incorporating a large workshop can be seen, together with a recovered Wey barge, the *Reliance*, built in Guildford in 1936 and the rotor of the Gilkes turbine rescued from Guildford Town Mill.

28 GUILDFORD: CRANE BASE

SU 961 924　　　　　　　　**✳**

A concrete base for a small crane beside head-race of the Town Mill. Pyramid-shaped with protruding screwed stud, probably for mounting a small crane for removing rubbish from the channel.

29 GUILDFORD: CANAL LOCKS

NT ✳

Locks for the Godalming Navigation are 1) by the Yvonne Arnaud Theatre (**SU 996 492**) and 2) at St Catherine's (**SU 995 477**). Also at St Catherine's are a turning roller and a lock keeper's cottage although this is not the original one. Locks for the Wey Navigation are 1) at Stoke Mill (**TQ 002 516**), 2) at Bower's Mill (**TQ 013 529**) and 3) at Pyrford (Newark) Mill (**TQ 043 569**).

30 GUILDFORD: FORMER LIME WHARF

SU 998 489　　　　　　　　**✳**

Site of John Davis' lime wharf but now the Guildford Boating Club. An old chalk wall survives. Now under water is the site of Loseley lime wharf at **SU 994 484**, in use from about 1800 to 1860.

31 PIRBRIGHT: DEEPCUT LOCKS

SU 911 566 to 896 567　　　　　**✳**

Deepcut Locks, Frimley Green. A cutting, 1000 yards and about 70 ft deep constructed in 1794 for the Basingstoke Canal with a flight of 14 locks to raise the canal by 95 ft. By Curzon Bridge (**SU 920 564**) is a high wall built to shield barge horses from the noise of the Woking to Southampton railway.

32 SEND: TURNING ROLLER

TQ 020 533　　　　　　　　**✳**

At Broad Oak bridge. Made of wood and mounted vertically to help horse-drawn barges on a sharp bend below Broad Oak bridge, built in 1849, which carries the drive to Sutton Place, the mansion of Sir Richard Weston, the pioneer of the Navigation.

33 SEND: WORSFOLD LOCK GATES
TQ 016 557   **NT** ✳
Potters Lane. Wooden lock gates fitted with simple peg and hole paddles. The purpose of these gates is to shut off the canal section, which begins here, in time of floods or to effect repairs to the canal bed. The gates are normally left open.

34 SEND: CANAL WORKSHOP
TQ 016 557   **NT** ✳
Wey Navigation workshop, near Cartbridge. Old and timber framed with original tools and equipment. Restored in 1991.

35 SHALFORD: GUNPOWDER STORAGE HUT
SU 998 466   **NT** ✳
Stonebridge Wharf, Godalming Navigation. A hut on staddle stones used for storing gunpowder in transit from Chilworth gunpowder works to the magazines at Barking on the Thames. Earlier it used to be brought to Dapdune Wharf, Guildford by wagon. The Wey & Arun Junction Canal joins the Navigation at SU 997 464.

CAR HISTORY

36 GUILDFORD: DENNIS VEHICLE WORKS
TQ 001 524   ■
Dennis Specialist Vehicles, Slyfield Green Trading Estate, is the latest version of the Dennis Brothers firm which was started by the two brothers, John and Raymond Dennis. John was first employed by Filmer & Mason but then went on to make his own bicycles in 1898 in a High Street shop. With his younger brother's help he subsequently made motorised tricycles and motorcars, until production ceased in 1913. After that, public service vehicles were made, such as fire engines and dust carts. Other products have been lawn mowers, cess-pool emptiers, buses, coaches and ambulances. During World War II, the Guildford factory made tanks, one of which is preserved in a military museum in Belgium. Two of the early cars, made respectively in 1903 and 1913, still belong to the Dennis family, and the Slyfield Green works retains a 1936 fire engine for active use.

37 GUILDFORD: RODBOROUGH BUILDINGS
SU 994 495   **LSII** ✳
Rodborough Buildings, Onslow Street, Guildford, is probably the oldest surviving purpose-built multi-storey car factory in Europe and possibly the world; it was erected in 1901 for Dennis Brothers but the firm moved to a larger site at Woodbridge Hill, Guildford, (SU 888 507) between 1905 and 1911 whereupon the Onslow Street building was used by the Rodboro Boot & Shoe Co and afterwards by an engineering firm making Mark Webber engines mostly sold to lifeboat stations for powering winches.

In 1985 the Woodbridge Hill site was sold for development as a business park and the making of fire engines for use round the world

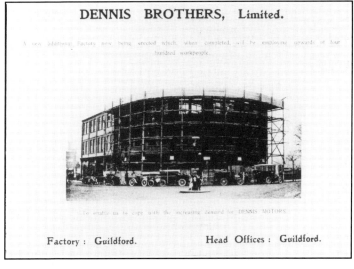

DENNIS BROTHERS, Limited.

Factory : Guildford.   Head Offices : Guildford.

37: Rodborough Buildings, Guildford
Reproduced by courtesy of the Surrey Record Office

7

has been continued by Dennis Specialist Vehicles Ltd at Slyfield Green. (See 36).

38 GUILDFORD: DENNISVILLE ESTATE

SU 984 497   ✳

Dennisville is an estate of 102 houses built to accommodate the workers of White and Poppe Ltd, Coventry, with whom Dennis Bros first joined forces in 1919 and which they then took over in 1933.

RAILWAYS

39 ASH: ENGINE SHED

SU 899 508   ✳

Next to the station. Both shed and station were built around 1900 and the shed was used by engines from the London & South Western Railway although the station was used by the South Eastern and Chatham Railway for the line to Guildford. The shed is now private property.

40 ASH GREEN: STATION

SU 906 504   ✳

The station remains but is a private house. The route of the old line is still visible from the nearby road bridge. The old route left the present Guildford-Aldershot line at Ash junction where the earthworks can still be traced.

41 CHILWORTH: RAILWAY ACCIDENT MEMORIAL

TQ 042 473

Memorial near site of Lockner Holt, com-memorating an accident in 1900 when a goods train broke in half and the guard was killed. The memorial is a yew tree cut to shape like a chair seat with a peacock over the top. It is regularly trimmed by permanent way staff.

42 GUILDFORD: MAIN STATION

SU 992 496   ✳

The original station buildings dating as far back as 1845 to 1884 and some rebuilt in 1888 have been swept away during major refurbishment in 1990-1. A few of the 1845 outbuildings survive, notably the blacksmith's workshop and the Farnham Road bridge. The site of the roundhouse or locomotive shed is now a large car park. Just south of the station the line goes through Chalk Tunnel (845 yards) and then St Catherine's Tunnel (132 yards) where in 1895 part of the tunnel roof collapsed. An empty train from Petersfield ran into the debris without taking any human life but two horses, which were stabled above the tunnel, were killed.

43 NORTH CAMP: STATION

SU 887 537   ✳

Lysons Avenue. Has extra long and deep platforms to accommodate trains carrying troops and horses.

44 PEASMARSH: EMBANKMENT

SU 992 470 to 999 471   ✳

Embankment of uncompleted spur line, 1860/1. To connect Godalming line to Redhill line but track was never laid.

42: Guildford roundhouse as it used to be.

Tony Martin Collection

45: Bisley Camp preserved railway station

Photo: Chris Shepheard

45 PIRBRIGHT: BISLEY CAMP LINE
SU 936 577 ☐

Unusual line serving the National Rifle Association's famous ranges at Bisley from 1890 to 1954. A sleeping car is preserved, together with the station buildings and platforms.

46 SHALFORD: LOCOMOTIVE AXLE
TQ 001 471 ✳

A vertical split axle–possibly from a broad gauge locomotive–along the footpath on Shalford Common. Located between the south wall of Shalford Cemetery and the railway cutting constructed in 1855. Its probable purpose was to attach a rope and operate a hoist with a horse and barrow; the material excavated was used in providing earth for the embankments at Peasmarsh.

47 TONGHAM: STATION
SU 887 491 ✳

Grange Rd. Station now demolished but the old platform can still be traced.

AIR TRANSPORT

48 WISLEY: AIRFIELD
TQ 075 576 ✳

Off A3 Portsmouth Road. Acquired by Vickers-Armstrong in 1943 when they needed a longer runway than was possible at Brooklands. Used extensively during World War II and afterwards when planes were taken from Brooklands to Wisley for final assembly and test flying.

---

2 WATERMILLS AND WINDMILLS

WATERMILLS

49 ALBURY: THE STREET
TQ 053 479 ✳

A five storey red brick building on a site recorded since 1255, used until lately as a Testing Laboratory. No trace of any machinery or wheel. A romantic story is often told about the mill, namely that about 1830 a young man named Warner was courting the miller's daughter but her father objected to the romance. Warner took his revenge by burning down the mill and was the last man in this country to be hanged for arson. The reality is that Warner fired the mill as part of a revolt by farm workers. The miller, James Franks, was overseer of the poor. Warner was executed in January 1831.

50 ALBURY: BOTTING'S MILL
TQ 039 480 ✳

In Mill Lane. A mill on this site was used for paper-making from 1809 to c.1876, followed by

50: Waterwheel at Bottings Mill, originally from the Clandon Estate *Drawing: P Watkins*

9

a flock mill. (See also its connection with the local manufacture of gunpowder in *Chilworth Gunpowder mills* by Glenys Crocker, page 37.) In 1910 Charles Botting erected the present buildings to house a roller corn mill powered by a turbine and latterly animal feed was produced. The mill closed in 1991. The fish farm in the grounds makes use of the water supply to breed trout for sale. A small cast-iron water wheel, made by Filmer and Mason at their foundry in Guildford and supplied .originally to the Clandon Park estate has been installed here by permission of Lord Onslow, after refurbishment by members of the Surrey Industrial History Group.

51 EASHING
SU 946 438   *

On the River Wey. Probably dating from before the Domesday Book survey. Both paper making and corn milling have been carried out together on this site–it was the second earliest paper mill in Surrey. It ceased working as a corn mill in 1832 when paper took over in importance and turbines later replaced the waterwheels. Pewtress Cottages (SU 946 436) were built for papermill workers by the firm of Pewtress & ·Co. It ceased working as a paper mill in 1889. Subsequently the buildings were sold to an engineering firm.

52 GOMSHALL
TQ 085 478   LSII *

On the Tillingbourne at a site where there has been a mill since before 1086 but it closed in 1953. It is now a restaurant but the wheel, which is 18ft diameter and 6ft wide, has been retained as a decorative feature.

53 GUILDFORD: TOWN MILL
SU 996 492   LSII *

In Millmead. There have been mills on or near this site since at least the Domesday Survey. One of the earliest references (1250) to a fulling mill in England suggests it was near this spot. The fine brick building was built between 1768 and 1770 and was extended to its present length in 1852 when the older wooden mills, built soon after the Civil War, were demolished. The new mill contained four pairs of stones and also a pump, powered by a water wheel, to supply the town with water from a reservoir at the foot of Pewley Hill, originally set up in 1701 by a William Yarnold. His Guildford Water Works was eventually bought by the Borough Council in 1866, together with the mill, and a new municipal reservoir was constructed at the very top of the Hill. The misleading plaque reading 1896 was affixed to the building when the Council installed new pumps and converted the mills as a water-works. In 1990 the Borough Council and the National Trust removed for restoration a two-tonne turbine made by Gilkes of Kendal in 1930 generating 68hp and used for pumping water up to the Pewley Hill reservoir. In 1966 the Water Board leased the mill to the newly opened Yvonne Arnaud Theatre as scenery workshops.

54 GUILDFORD: STOKE MILL
SU 998 510   ■

Woking Road. A strongly built five-storey Victorian mill on the River Wey. The Domesday Survey of 1086 recorded a corn mill on the site and since then there have been fulling and paper mills here. One of these, built by Sir Richard Weston, in 1633, was the earliest of the 30 or so paper mills in Surrey. The present building dates from 1879 when traditional mill stones were being replaced by iron rollers which crushed rather than cut the grain. It was powered originally by a water wheel but subsequently by water turbines, one of which has been repainted and is now exhibited in front of the building, and a further damaged one can be found in the undergrowth on the downstream bank. The adjoining single-storey building (1863) was built as a half-stuff mill for

54: The re-furbished Stoke Mill
Photo: Chris Shepheard

Eashing paper mill (see 51) but became a store for the corn mill in 1869. The mill ceased operating in 1957 but was later used for paint manufacture. No machinery remains in the mill which has been excellently restored as offices.

55 GOMSHALL: NETLEY MILL
TQ 079 479

Downstream from Gomshall Mill but irregularly used. In 1233 a mill here belonged to the Abbey of Netley near Southampton which is how it got its name. In the 18th century, it was rebuilt in the style of a folly with a ruined tower and pointed window arches. Originally it used a large breastshot wheel which was replaced with an overshot: it ceased working as a mill in 1907 but later was used as a pumping station by the Hurtwood Water Co.

56 OCKHAM
TQ 056 579　　　　　　　　　　　　*

Mills have existed here since 1296. The present mill is a four-storeyed one dating from 1862 and is decorated in the style of the properties-belonging to the Earl of Lovelace with terracotta tiles and incised patterns. The mill stopped working in 1927 and is now a private house but restoration work to the surviving machinery is continuing. There is an internal waterwheel of 14ft 6in diameter and 9ft 10in wide; the iron shaft was made by Filmer & Mason of Guildford in 1880. A sluice gate is inscribed **LORD LOVELACE 1841**.

57 PIRBRIGHT
SU 942 554　　　　　　　　　　　　■

Adjacent to Mill Lane. Documented in 1729 but most of the mill is of a later date. At one time it had been used as a saw mill but it ceased operations in 1939. Most of the machinery remains; the iron overshot wheel has been rebuilt and the mill converted to residential accomodation.

58 PYRFORD: NEWARK MILL
TQ 040 575　　　　　　　　　　　　*

Although the millhouse and various outbuildings survive, the mill itself was destroyed by fire in 1965; it was probably the oldest existing mill building in Surrey. A mill here was mentioned in the Domesday Survey of Send and thus predates Newark Priory, whose ruins are nearby and which was established between 1170 and 1220. The mill may have been rebuilt when the Navigation Canal was cut in 1653. Before its destruction, it contained three large separate waterwheels.

A drainage channel nearby contains an eel trap, a long iron and brick cage bearing the date 1818 with holes leading to a collecting pit.

59 SHALFORD: THE STREET
TQ 001 476　　　　　　　　　　**LSII NT** ☐

A picturesque timber-framed building owned by the National Trust. Although on a 14th century site, it dates from the early 18th century and was presented to the Trust in

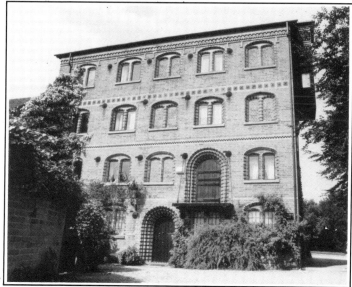

56: Ockham Mill
Photo: Chris Shepheard

1932 by an anonymous group calling themselves 'Ferguson's Gang'. The mill had worked until 1914 and still contains an excellent collection of machinery. The low breastshot waterwheel of 12ft diameter however was damaged in floods and lacks its lower half, although the Trust hopes to repair it when funds become available. The storage area, about half of the total building, has been converted into a house.

60 WEST HORSLEY
TQ 080 541 ■

Behind Roundtree Farmhouse are the remains of the old mill pond. A mill was recorded in Domesday Book and belonged to the manor of Lollesworth. It was last mentioned in 1888 as a cider mill.

61 WORPLESDON: RICKFORD MILL
SU 965 546   LSII ■

Situated on the Stanford Brook, its documented history starts in 1833. The present four-storeyed brick building is believed to be of 18th century origin but is now a private house, with some of the machinery retained in the drawing room. In 1906 the waterwheel was replaced by a 25in Armfield turbine; milling

ended in about 1959. There was a mill making blankets until the beginning of the 19th century at Goose Rye, downstream from Rickford Mill.

WINDMILLS

The acknowledged reference book for the windmills of Surrey is by Farries and Mason, *The Windmills of Surrey and Inner London*, (1966). For the Guildford Borough area, it discusses evidence for the existence of windmills at Ash, Frimley, Guildford, Pirbright, and West Horsley. Only Frimley and West Horsley have visible remains.

62 FRIMLEY
TQ 896 563 ■

A tower windmill of red brick, first mentioned in 1784. Disused by 1870 but incorporated in 1914 into a modern house called The Old Mill sited on a ridge off the old Guildford road.

63 WEST HORSLEY
TQ 080 521 ■

A towermill 330 yards SW of the crossroads was marked on maps from 1729 to 1842. The site has been levelled but a Derbyshire millstone survives.

---

3 PUBLIC UTILITIES AND PRIVATE SUPPLIES

WATER

ALBURY: FARM ESTATE PUMPS ■

The Albury Estate (belonging to The Northumberland Estates) has a number of old pumps and machinery. These include

64 (TQ 062 484) An 8hp turbine installed in 1880 by Green and Carter at Home Farm Buildings, Shere Rd, Albury (See also 132). Not in working order. Its purpose was to drive agricultural machinery such as a mangle grinder and chaff cutter in a nearby building by means of a 30 ft steel shaft.

65 (TQ 044 476) A 7ft by 2ft undershot water wheel at Vale End, Albury, now converted into a trout fishery. Powered by the Tillingbourne, it drove a 2.5in x 6in two throw pump, **12** installed by Green and Carter about 1880.

Taking water from a nearby artesian well, it formerly supplied the village of Albury with its water. The water wheel still works but the pump has been vandalised.

65: Water wheel on the Albury Estate
Photo: Glenys Crocker

66 (TQ 058 479) A 21in vertical turbine at Weston Lake, Albury, installed by Green and Carter in 1948, raising 600 gallons per hour to 400 ft. Though no longer in use, it was employed to pump water from a well to supply Estate farms.

67 (TQ 060 484) Remains of 2 old Green and Carter pumps with Brook electric motor and Lister D engine at Sherbourne Farm, Albury. Placed by a reservoir to supply the farm.

68 WEST HORSLEY: WELL
TQ 103 525   ✻

Wooden well structure situated at Park Horsley. Shingle type roof of steeple type, housing old well winding mechanism—iron handle and two gear wheels.

69 EFFINGHAM: PUMPS
TQ 118 532   ■

St Teresa's School. Water Tower, hand pump and dismantled pump. Another hand pump in old stables courtyard. Cast iron without maker's name but with some ornamentation. Water tower is said to hold about 10,000 gallons of water, now pumped from the mains.

70 GUILDFORD: WATERWORKS
SU 995 493   ✻

Beside Yvonne Arnaud Theatre and at Pewley Down. In 1701 William Yarnold was authorised to erect a pump driven by a water wheel at the east end of the fulling mill beside the present theatre. The water was raised to an open reservoir at the bottom of Pewley Hill. Subsequent reservoirs were built in 1853 and 1866, each higher on Pewley Hill than the one before. Water was pumped from the Town Mill in wooden pipes. When the Pewley Hill reservoir was made ' in 1866, water was pumped by |a steam engine| situated| at Mill-mead. A turbine has recently been removed from the Town Mill where it was used for pumping water.

71 GUILDFORD: PUMP
SU 893 484   ■

Horse gin 200 yards north of the Hog's Back Hotel, which was originally Poyle House, on the A31 road. The driving gear is 8ft from the well, which has a three-throw pump, and is inscribed J TAYLOR & SONS PATENT, 2 NEWGATE STREET, LONDON.

72 OCKHAM: PUMPING HOUSE
TQ 089 581   ■

For pumping water to Hatchford House. Remains of brick hexagonal building covering an artesian well said to be over 600 ft deep.

There may have been a well worked by a windlass and donkey followed by a donkey or horse whim to pump water 250 yards to a brick built storage tank. Probably unused since 1939. The tank, with|claimed capacity of 12,000 gallons, used to supply the whole village.

73 WEST HORSLEY: PUMPING STATION
TQ 079 523   ✻

On the A246 road. A small 1893 pumping station of the Woking Water & Gas Co with engine house and chimney stack. Brick built with cast iron rounded windows.

ELECTRICITY
74 GUILDFORD: FORMER ELECTRICITY WORKS
SU 994 495   ✻

The Wharf. The shell of a small brick-built generating station which displays the date of 1913. One of the oldest surviving buildings of this sort in this country but plans exist for redevelopment of the site. The Guildford Electric Supply Company began in 1896 but it was taken over by the Corporation in 1921 who built a larger generating station off the Woodbridge Road (**SU 993 505**). This was demolished in 1970 but traces can still be found of the cooling water inlet and coal berth.

GAS

75 GUILDFORD: GAS LAMP STANDARD
TQ 998 493   ✻

Beside Castle bowling green and the bandstand entrance (*see right*). Dates from about 1830. A fluted stone pillar in Doric style with a crevice for the gas pipe to reach the top. Originally placed at the extremity of the gas lighting system—which was started in 1824—at the junction of Upper High Street and Epsom Road.

Photo: Chris Shepheard

13

76 CHILWORTH: GUNPOWDER MILLS

TQ 023 473–TQ 040 480 |SC(part) part ■ part *

See article by Glenys Crocker, pages 37.

77 GOMSHALL: TANNERY

TQ 086 478 *

Tanning was an important local industry in the Guildford and Godalming areas and had a close relationship with the sheep and woollen trades. The last Godalming tannery closed in the 1950s but Gomshall tannery having been modernised after the Second World War continued until 1988. There are some 19th century and earlier timber framed buildings including a former bark store and a medieval packhorse bridge (Site no. 14). Damaged by fire in 1992.

78 GUILDFORD: IRON WORKS

SU 997 497 *

Bellerby Theatre, Leapale Lane, formerly the Church Acre iron works, built in 1868 for Filmer & Mason on what was then known as Madhouse Lane because of a private lunatic asylum nearby. The three large bays that still survive have an arrangement of beams and braces typical of the industrial roof-trusses of the mid-Victorian era. Particularly of note are the two delicately designed iron grills which ventilate the buildings, in the gable ends. Also active on this site were Mark Webber Ltd, later known as Webber Engineering Ltd, who made petrol, gas or paraffin powered stationary engines to drive dynamos, winches (including many lifeboat winches) and water pumps.

The firm existed from 1919 to 1934 first at Leapale Lane, then at Rodboro Buildings in Bridge Street where they were taken over by J I Blackburn & Co who moved their operations to Catteshall Mill, Godalming, in 1939.

79 GUILDFORD: CLOTH FACTORY

SU 998 496 LSII *

Cloth Hall, North Street. Now a retail store but originally a factory built in 1629 by George Abbott, a local clothworker's son who became Archbishop of Canterbury. Hoping to replace wool, he subsidised linen weaving in an unsuccessful attempt to revive the town's declining textile industry. The building became a house for paupers in 1656 and a school from 1856 when the tower was added.

80 GUILDFORD: NEWSPAPER OFFICES

SU 999 497 *

No. 62 Chertsey Street. Until very recently, the offices of the *Guildford Times* paper, established in 1855.

81 GUILDFORD: ENGINEERING WORKS

SU 968 512

Drummonds Engineering (Staveley), Broad Street. 1888–1982. Famous for its lathes (especially the 4" type favoured by model makers) and gear-shaping machines.

82 GUILDFORD: TIMBER MERCHANTS

SU 993 505 *

John Moon & Co (now Harcros Ltd), Walnut Tree Close. Timber merchants since 1848.

78: Bellerby Theatre, Guildford. Part of the former ironworks *Photo: Chris Shepheard*

Until 1956 the company was based at Millmead, on the site where Debenhams now stands. Wood was taken in barges up river from the London docks.

83 GUILDFORD: MEDIEVAL CLOTH INDUSTRY
SU 999 494 ☐

Racks Close. When the cloth industry was all important to the area, racks or tentering frames on which cloth was stretched to dry after being dyed—often with woad to produce the famous 'Guildford Blue' cloth—were placed here. Near at hand are the (blocked) entrances to mines where a hard chalk known as clunch was taken for a building stone.

84 GUILDFORD: ENGINEERING WORKS
SU 993 495 ✳

Clark and Gammon auction rooms, Bedford Road, was formerly the Skelton engineering works from 1885. This firm has now moved to Slyfield Green Industrial Estate, Guildford.

85 GUILDFORD: BOTTLING PLANT
SU 997 498 ✳

The former Unigate bottling plant in Chertsey Street used to be a lemonade bottling factory for R W White & Sons Ltd from 1899 to 1925; then it was subsequently used as a dairy depot until 1989. The facade and skeleton of the building have been kept whilst the rest has been re-built.

86 GUILDFORD: NEWSPAPER OFFICES
SU 997 497 ✳

Surrey Advertiser newspaper offices, Martyr Road. Starting life in 1864 as a monthly advertising paper for West Surrey, it grew into a weekly newspaper and changed premises many times until 1937 when it moved into its

86: The Surrey Advertiser Building, Guildford
Photo: Chris Shepheard

present building—an interesting example of 1930's industrial architecture.

87 GUILDFORD: WAREHOUSES
SU 992 497 ✳

Walnut Tree Close. Erected from 1856 onwards for Joseph Billing whose London Printing Works specialised in printing Bibles for the British and Foreign Bible Society. His prosperity led to the expansion of the buildings on at least seven occasions until the firm moved to new buildings in 1962 and the old buildings were let as warehouses. They have recently been refurbished. The firm also pursued an enlightened policy about housing their workers. From 1906 to 1924 they built 24 semi-detached houses at Weston Road, Woodbridge Hill, Guildford, through their 'Caxton Gardens Cottage Club' because the firm was aware that Guildford rents reached 'a distinctly higher level than in many other towns of similar character'. The worker had to pay merely sixpence a week more than for other rented accommodation over twenty years.

88 GUILDFORD: FOUNDRY SITE
SU 995 493 ✳

Yvonne Arnaud Theatre, site of the Guildford Foundry, set up in 1794 by E Filmer who with a partner made iron castings. Later the firm made all the castings for the Portsmouth railway line and reached the height of its prosperity from 1854 to 1883 as Filmer & Mason. Many later changes of name and occupancy happened, including for example, Weyman & Co (1885 to 1895) who made the Trusty gas engine for John Henry Knight of Farnham, a pioneer of the motor car. The Millmead foundry was finally knocked down in 1941.

78: A Mark Webber engine, a print from an original block advert   *Tony Harcombe Collection*

15

89 SHALFORD: FIBRE MAKERS
SU 997 467   ✳

Spaulding Russell site. Just south of Broadford Bridge, originally on the site of the burnt-out Broadford Brewery; Mr Filmer Jacobs in 1927 started to make vulcanised fibre from chemically treated paper, which was used for many items from washers to wartime jettison petrol tanks for Spitfires. In 1967 the company was taken over and became Spaulding Russell, part of the largest independent firm of paper makers in the UK. Ceased trading in 1984. Some of the steam engines and machinery have been preserved by the Ben Turner Group of Ripley. All buildings on the site demolished in 1985 and replaced by buildings of ultra-modern design, including one which has recently housed Ferrari Cars' design centre.

90 SHERE: CLOTH INDUSTRY
TQ 074 476   ✳

The Spinning Walk and Rack Close are roads on the southern edge of the village which commemorate the times when it was known for its manufacture of fustian, a mixture of cotton and linen. A number of other houses in the village were occupied by weavers, eg Tudor Cottage, Lime Cottage and Denton in Upper Street, and the present Post Office in Middle Street.

5 MINERAL EXTRACTION

Information and notes supplied by Richard Williams

CHALK EXTRACTION AND LIMEBURNING

Chalk extraction is one of the oldest industries of the Guildford area. Disused chalk mines have been proved to lie under the hillside on which Guildford stands; the best known are the 'Caverns' running from Racks Close under Castle Cliffe Gardens. These produced a hard chalk known as 'clunch' used as a building stone, eg in Guildford Castle Palace. Racks Close itself is probably the oldest open chalkpit and its chalk would have been burnt into lime for making mortar, but its origin is undated. The 1992 excavations of the Guildford Castle Palace are expected to prove whether a walled pit found in the previous year was indeed a limekiln of the early 13th century as suspected. The earliest lime-kiln found so far in Guildford was in the grounds of Westbury House, Millmead, dated to the 12th century–perhaps used in building the first St Nicholas Church. An early documentary reference to lime burning is contained in the Account Book for the building of Loseley House in 1561-9 which shows that chalk was extracted from a quarry in Guildford rented by Sir William More and carted to limekilns erected on Losely land for making mortar. These accounts also refer to mortar from Albury, implying limeburning was carried on there at this early date. Clunch was used in private houses, e.g. for ornamental fireplaces, as in Castle Arch, Quarry Street, now Guildford Museum, and Surrey Archaeological Society's offices.

The expansion of brick house-building in Surrey in the 17th century and through the 18th century, including many large country houses, would have created a large demand for mortar. Lime was also used for whitewashing and in the tanning and paper making industries. Good water transport along the Wey Navigation to the Thames led to Guildford chalk and lime being shipped to London for the building industry in the 18th century but 'grey chalk' from the geological Lower Chalk made better, more waterproof, lime mortar and this is scarce in the Guildford area due to faulting. The grey chalk exposures are more extensive in the Dorking area and further east, so that Dorking lime was bought in preference to Guildford, although it meant transport by road to Kingston. In the early 19th century, the 'riverage' charges on the Wey Navigation also made the Guildford chalk and lime less competitive, as revealed by surviving correspondence between the lessees of chalkpits and the Wey proprietors, and the extension of the Surrey Iron Railway in 1805 allowed Merstham to compete for London markets. About 1821, lime from Kent was supplied more cheaply by being taken down the Medway and up the Thames by sailing barge, requiring no horses and paying no canal dues. The Guildford industry turned increasingly towards supplying the needs of agriculture, making lime in kilns at the quarries or selling raw chalk to be burnt in kilns on or near the farms on greensand or clay soils, using both road and canal transport.

Limeburning declined rapidly after 1850 owing to rail transport allowing the large manufacturers to deliver their lime and ground chalk over a wide area, although local kilns continued to be used by farmers to the end of the century or even later. The introduction of artificial fertilisers caused a further decline in limeburning, leaving only a small number of the larger quarries operating into modern times.

SITES OF CHALKPITS/LIMEWORKS

There are many chalkpits along the North Downs, some long disused and overgrown. The following list concentrates on ones where limeburning is known or is likely to have been carried out. Dates shown are those of the earliest indication known from maps or documents. Grid references define quarried areas approximately as they are often extensive.

91 ALBURY: WATER LANE
TQ 046 488

Small chalkpit, of interest as a limekiln of small field-kiln type converted into a gun-post c1940. Unfortunately now buried under a tip.

92 ALBURY: CHALKPITS
TQ 061 489 *

Long disused.

TQ 061 487 *

Partly intact kiln to S. beside bridle path, shown on 1782 Albury estate map. A World War II spigot mortar platform is built on top of the kiln and a pillbox stands beside it.

92: Albury lime kiln   *Drawing: P Watkins*

93 GUILDFORD: ST CATHERINE'S
SU 993 487 ■

Off Guildown Rd.

94 GUILDFORD: LANGTON PRIORY
SU 994 485 ■

Limeburning from before 1783 to c1853. Kilns destroyed by development.

95 GUILDFORD: LOSELEY LIME WHARF
SU 994 484

Site of the wharf. Some Lower Chalk (grey chalk) suitable for making good mortar is exposed at Langton Priory and was exploited up to the 1820s.

96 GUILDFORD: ECHO PIT
TQ 004 489 ■

Shown on 1768 Rocque map. No kilns known.

97 GUILDFORD: SOUTH WARREN FARM
TQ 007 485 ■

Grey chalk quarry had large kiln block shown on Tithe Map 1842. Some visible brickwork remains.

98 GUILDFORD: FOXENDEN QUARRY
SU 999 498 *

Disused by 1870.

99 GUILDFORD: RAILWAY STATION AREA
SU 992 494 and 992 497 *

Two kilns shown on 1870 map.

100 GUILDFORD: SHALFORD ROAD
SU 999 489 ■

'Upper Quarry' ('Great Quarry' today) and 'Lower Quarry' (SU 999 487). 1729. Limekiln House (now Quarry Cottage) pre-1837 at junction of Shalford Road and Chantry View Road. Three bottle kilns stood to S of house; one is partly preserved. Remains of rectangular kiln with two drawholes in middle of Lower Quarry dates from c1850 (on private property).

101 GUILDFORD: SHALFORD ROAD
SU 997 489 *

Site of lime wharf now occupied by Guildford Rowing Club. Earliest reference to chalk-**17** pits–1650; to limeburning–1775 (in a contemporary watercolour); sale of two kilns recorded–1783.

102 PUTTENHAM: COMPTON
SU 943 to 952 483 *
Extensive quarrying area on S slope of Hog's Back (1729–1811).

103 SEALE: HOG'S BACK
SU 889 481 and 890 480 ■
On S slope. Kilns shown on 1882 OS map and lime works 1913.

104 SEALE: HOG'S BACK
SU 899 482 ■
On S side. Three kilns shown on 1882 OS at W end, now completely destroyed by landscaping. One kiln shown in E part of quarry survives largely intact on Surrey Wildlife Trust land.

105 SHERE
TQ 068 487 ■
A kiln dating from 1823.

106 SHERE
TQ 068 485
Kiln shown on 1871 OS map; no visible remains.

107 SHERE
TQ 073 485 *
A largely intact well-built kiln stands near an old chalkpit and shows good example of glaze on brick lining.

108 SHERE
TQ 085 486
Near Colekitchen Farm. 1725-1811-1895. Limekiln shown on 1725 estate map. No surviving remains.

109 WANBOROUGH
■
Several chalkpits at SU 935 488, 947 489, and 956 489. Possible limekiln base used as incinerator at first-named site.

110 WEST CLANDON
TQ 041 509 ■
S side of A246 road. 1729.

111 WEST CLANDON
TQ 040 509 ■
A modern quarry still open.

112 WEST HORSLEY
TQ 079 520 ■
1729. Sale document of 1657 refers to a limeburner of West Horsley near. Kiln shown on 1934 map may now only be represented by brick rubble. Limekilns marked on 1823 map.

FIELD KILNS

During the 18th and early 19th centuries, many farms had their own small kilns for local limeburning, using furze grown locally as fuel. They went out of use as finely ground chalk became available and bulk supplies of lime by rail and road became economic. Some would have been communal and those referred to above in or near chalkpits at Albury and Shere were probably so, for the use of farms near the chalk. They were generally inefficient being of a simple design of sandstone with a hard brick lining and a single draw hole. Rather than tapering almost to a point, as an efficient bottle kiln did, they narrow only slightly to a brick platform at the base, and loading had to commence by forming an arch of chalk blocks supported on this platform. A model of one excavated on Smarts Heath, Woking, is held by the Guildford Museum.

The following are examples with significant remains.

113 ALBURY
TQ 055 442 *
Near Mayorhouse Farm. Substantial remains. About 100m to SSW is another, largely buried but with front wall visible.

114 ALBURY
TQ 049 450 ■
Rompin Downs. Partly intact but damaged by tree growth and fallen trees.

115 ALBURY
TQ 055 467 *
At Kiln Rough, Albury Heath. Front wall rebuilt without buttresses, rest of kiln buried.

116 PUTTENHAM
SU 927 480 ■
Intact but filled with rubbish. Stands near edge of hopfield with small chalkpit nearby.

116: Puttenham lime kiln   *Photo: Chris Shepheard*

OTHER SITES
117 COMPTON
SU 958 478   ✳

Pottery associated with the Watts Gallery, Down Lane. The wife of the great Victorian painter, G F Watts, discovered a seam of clay, perfect for modelling and potting in 1890. Having designed the Watts Mortuary Chapel in Art Nouveau/Celtic style, she taught the people of Compton to model the decorations required for it, and in 1889 started the commercial Pottery. The original building burnt down in 1923 but was replaced. The clay ran out in 1937 and Mrs Watts died in 1938. The Pottery closed finally in the 1950s.

118 WANBOROUGH
SU 957 489   ■

Chalk pit, Hog's Back, East Flexford.

119 WANBOROUGH
SU 924 497   ✳

Flexford brickworks chimney. 19th century.

120 WORPLESDON
SU 976 522

Keen's brickworks. From 1850 to 1941 a brickyard specialising in high class bricks and tiles. The workings and a pond have been filled in and houses built there.

117: Detail from Watts Chapel, Compton. Decoration over the main door
Photo: Chris Shepheard

6 FOOD AND DRINK

DOVECOTES
121 ALBURY: WESTON YARD
TQ 053 478   LSII ■

An octagonal brick dovecote of 24 ft diameter from about 1550, complete with interior potence to reach the 300 nests. Recently restored by the Albury Trust and awarded a plaque for conservation by the Surrey Industrial History Group.

122 CLANDON: CLANDON PARK HOUSE
TQ 044 512   ❐

18th century.

123 GUILDFORD: MOUNT BROWNE
TQ 988 479   ■

Though now the headquarters of Surrey police, the house was originally the home of the third Marquis of Sligo. Well-made 19th century brick octagonal dovecote surmounted by windvane in corner of walled garden

124 GUILDFORD: LOSELEY HOUSE, ARTINGTON
TQ 975 472   LSII ❐

17th century.

125 EASHING: EASHING LANE, UPPER EASHING
TQ 949 434   ■

Belonging to Eashing House. 18th century.

126 EAST HORSLEY: HAMMONDS FARM, RIPLEY LANE
TQ 074 531   ■

17th century.

19

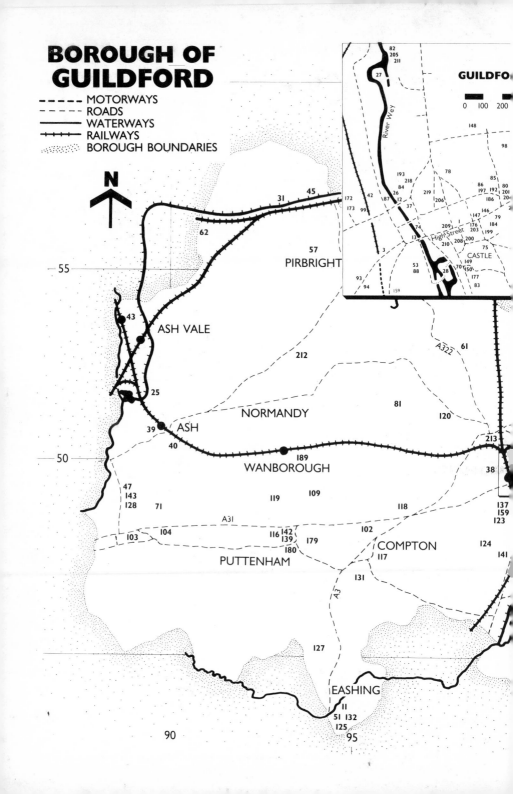

BOROUGH OF GUILDFORD

- ----- MOTORWAYS
- ----- ROADS
- ——— WATERWAYS
- +++++ RAILWAYS
- ::::::::: BOROUGH BOUNDARIES

N

GUILDFO

0   100   200

82
205
211

27

148

98

193   78
218   85
84   86   80
26   219   197 192 201
187   12   206   186   204

172   42
173   99

146
147   79
74   176   184
13   209   203   199
210   208   200
75
CASTLE
149
53   150
88   28   70   177
83

31   45

62

57

PIRBRIGHT

3

93
94   159

55

43

ASH VALE

212

A322   61

25

NORMANDY

81

120

39   **ASH**

40

213

50

WANBOROUGH

189

38

47
143
128   71

119   109

118

137
159
123

A31

103   104

116 142
139
180   179

102

COMPTON

124

141

PUTTENHAM

117

131

A3

127

EASHING

11

51 132
125

90

95

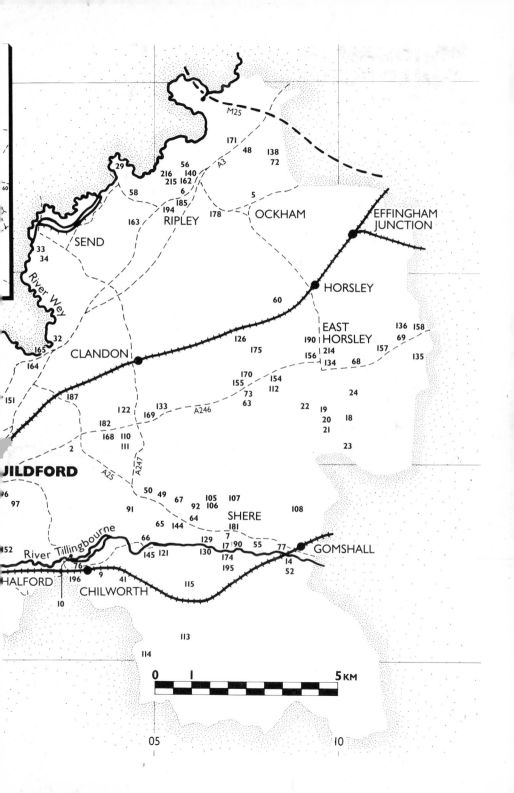

121: Restored Tudor dovecote at
Albury   *Drawing: P Watkins*

130 ALBURY: WESTON HOUSE

TQ 053 478 ■

In the garden of the house. ?17th century. A box-like room with walls, ceiling and floor of local iron-stone bonded like bricks, approximately 7 ft by 7ft ; floor of flints. Now without a superstructure having been used as a rubbish receptacle. Ice probably from the Tillingbourne.

131 COMPTON: EASTBURY MANOR

SU 954 470 ✳

Sited some distance from the house, (close to a footpath called Ice-House Lane) and in dangerous state.

132 EASHING: EASHING LANE

SU 949 435 ■

Formerly Eashing House which was demolished in 1947. Red brick in good condition but the entrance has been blocked up because of vandalism. It measures 8ft by 6ft the entrance lobby with a pit 9ft 4in across and 21ft deep. Believed to have been in use until the 1920s.

133 EAST CLANDON: HATCHLANDS

TQ 067 519 ⧠

Situated approximately 300 yds from the house on edge of old chalkpit with (now dry) pond at the bottom. Possibly contemporary with the house (1757). Imposing classical facade and dome over partially plastered and brick-lined pit, 30 ft deep. Once used as a summerhouse with a wooden floor.

134 EAST HORSLEY: HORSLEY TOWERS

TQ 099 528 ■

The covering mound is visible from the Guildford Road.

135 EFFINGHAM: GOLF COURSE

TQ 113 525 ✳

In the grounds, near road to Ranmore. The Golf Club house was originally the Manor House. In poor condition–hole knocked in roof and used for burning rubbish. Brickwork of entrance carried out with elaborate care.

127 SHACKLEFORD: ALDRO SCHOOL

TQ 934 455 ✳

Formerly known as Hall Place, the present school buildings date from the 1890s. Near the front entrance is a small, elegant, brick built, three tiered building, probably first constructed in Tudor times and altered several times since, becoming in turns a granary, a dovehouse and a cider press. It is now used by the school. Another small building nearby was a brewhouse. The original stables, converted into living quarters, has a turret clock of 1750 refurbished in 1896 by Benson of Ludgate Hill.

128 TONGHAM: THE STREET

SU 886 484 ■

17th century, part of Manor Farm.

ICEHOUSES

129 ALBURY: ALBURY PARK

TQ 063 477 ■

22 Possibly of 17th century. Situated close to where some Victorian larders were built into the bank.

136 EFFINGHAM: ST TERESA'S CONVENT SCHOOL

TQ 118 511 ■

Formerly Effingham East Court. Bricked up because of danger to children but entrance now used as shrine to Virgin Mary.

137 GUILDFORD: ST NICHOLAS, LANGTON PRIORY

SU 995 487 ■

Built into a complex of tunnels at different levels probably in connection with the early 19th century use of the site as lime quarry. The ice-house was probably inserted into the existing tunnels later in the 19th century but could have been a converted lime-kiln. The egg-shaped ice-house is 3.7m high with a maximum 2.5m diameter and is reached by steps leading upwards between brick walls from the side of the tunnels.

138 OCKHAM: HATCHFORD HOUSE

TQ 092 584 ■

Formerly Hatchford Park. Very large, brick built, 50 ft deep and 20 ft across. No obvious source of ice. Early 19th century.

139 PUTTENHAM: PRIORY

SU 934 477 ■

Built in 1719. Approached by path ascending up the side of a very large earthen mound close to the 'Priory' building. About 40 ft deep of brick construction with door missing. No obvious source of ice.

140 RIPLEY: LAMBART'S HILL

TQ 059 565 ✻

Originally belonging to Ockham Park. By wall bounding on old course of A3 road at Lambarts Hill. Probably 19th century construction during time of Lovelace family's ownership of estate. 16 ft deep and 12 ft in diameter. Said to have had a post-medieval vaulted roof. With top opening 'stopper' as well as usual entrance. Bricks made on estate's own brickworks. Ice obtained from pond 600 yds away, which, according to local stories, was stocked with rudd, eventually used as fish manure for the estate's orangery.

141 SHALFORD: SITE OF SHALFORD HOUSE

SU 998 477 ■

The House (18th century) was demolished to build new water board pumping station. Only small depression in ground now visible of the ice house.

MALTINGS & HOPKILNS

142 PUTTENHAM: THE STREET

SU 934 479 ✻

Hopkilns converted into residential accommodation.

143 TONGHAM: TONGHAM ROAD

SU 886 489 ✻

Maltings. Twin towered and brick built, showing many signs of repairs over the years. Now used by light engineering works.

MODEL FARMS

144 ALBURY: HOME FARM

TQ 062 483 ✻

Model farm of 1876 inherited by the 6th Duke of Northumberland through his marriage to the daughter of Henry Drummond, the banker. An imitation of Queen Victoria's Windsor Home Farm.

142: Converted hop kiln at Puttenham

Photo: Chris Shepheard

23

145 ALBURY: SIGN POST

TQ 048 478 ✻

Lamp standard and sign post at junction of The Street and Church Lane. Six-sided, carved before 1900 from an oak tree grown on the Albury Estate, by John Stanton Browne in the Albury Estate workshops. The three iron brackets· supporting sign boards and a metal finial were made by the local blacksmith.

146 GUILDFORD: CARVING

SU 998 495 ✻

Wooden carving on the exterior of Guildford House, 155 High St. Built in 1660. 'The best of the very individual late 17th century Guildford houses'–Pevsner: *The Buildings Of England*.

147 GUILDFORD: TOWN CLOCK

SU 998 495 LSII SC ✻

High St. The very ornate clock projecting over the road is the famous feature which signifies Guildford on photographs. Reputedly by John Aylward of London who gave it to the town in 1683 in order to be allowed to practice his trade here. Tunsgate, the ·Tuscan portico

opposite, was part of the Corn Exchange (1818), but the columns were moved in 1936-7 to allow vehicles through. The road surface of the High Street is maintained with granite sets.

148 GUILDFORD: COAL HOLE COVERS

SU 997 501 ✻

Stoke Fields. Eight cast iron coal hole covers of interesting design outside the front entrances of 19th century cottages. Many further covers are to be found in Guildford streets of 19th century artisan houses with little or no front gardens, or shops, such as the following locations in the centre of the town, High Street, Chapel Street, Castle Street, Quarry Street, Mill Lane, and Martyr Road, and many of the roads joining the old Stoke village to the town itself, such as Stoke Road, Dapdune Road, Drummond Road, and Artillery Terrace.

149 GUILDFORD: INSURANCE SIGN

SU 996 493 ✻

17 Quarry Street. Sun Insurance Co's firemark, c1799.

150 GUILDFORD: HERALDIC SIGN

SU 996 494 ✻

60-61 Quarry Street. Three gryphons of the Tallow Chandlers' Co. arms.

151 GUILDFORD: PILLAR BOX

TQ 016 520 ✻

Edward VIII pillar box, London Road, Burpham. One of the few erected in the country.

152 SHALFORD: FIRE INSURANCE SIGNS

TQ 001 477 ✻

Firemarks, Shalford Mill. One from the County Fire Office and one from the Sun Fire Insurance.

153 SHALFORD: STREET FURNITURE

TQ 001 469 ✻

Horse trough and drinking fountain erected by the people of Shalford to commemorate the 60th year of Queen Victoria's reign.

154 WEST HORSLEY: STREET FURNITURE

TQ 079 522 ✻

Trough and drinking fountain, 1909.

24 145: Albury, sign post and lamp finial
Photo: Chris Shepheard

147: Clock, Guildford High Street
Tony Martin Collection

151: Edward VIII pillar box, Burpham
Drawing: P Watkins

MILESTONES

155 EAST CLANDON
TQ 065 516 ✱
On A 246 between East Clandon and West Horsley. LONDON 26 LEATHERHEAD 7-2 GUILDFORD 4.

156 EAST HORSLEY
TQ 095 527 ✱
On north side of A 246 and east of bus stop lay-by and inset into the garden wall of the *Duke of Wellington* public house. LONDON 24 LEATHERHEAD 6-2 GUILDFORD 6

157 EFFINGHAM (1)
TQ 109 526 ✱
On north side of A 246 towards western end of the village near 'The Beeches'. GUILDFORD 7, LEATHERHEAD 4¹/₂.

158 EFFINGHAM (2)
TQ 122 534 ✱
On north side of A 246 about 30 yards west of junction with Orchard Gardens. GUILD-FORD 8, LEATHERHEAD 3¹/₂. (The positioning of the lettering on the stone suggests that it was originally situated on the opposite side of the road). *for drawing see page 26*

159 GUILDFORD (1)
SU 993 486 ✱
On A 3100 Portsmouth Rd between junctions with Chestnut Avenue and Guildown. Very worn, only figure 28 visible of the original legend LONDON 28, GODALMING 3, GUILDFORD 1.

160 GUILDFORD (2)
TQ 004 496 ✱
Beside gate of No.46 Epsom Rd. built into garden wall. The stone is weathered and the inscription is unreadable.

161 GUILDFORD (3)
TQ 011 509 ✱
At junction of Boxgrove Rd and London Rd to the south of the roundabout. In good condition. PORTSMOUTH 43, HYDE PARK CORNER 26, GUILDFORD 1, RIPLEY 5.

162 OCKHAM
TQ 070 581 ✱
On A3 at foot of Lambarts Hill (just north of Ripley/Ockham boundary). HYDE PARK CORNER 21.

163 RIPLEY
TQ 045 561 ✱
On A3 just south of Grove Heath North. HYDE PARK CORNER 22.

164 SEND (1)
TQ 029 535 ✱
On A3 on Ripley side of junction with Potters Lane. HYDE PARK CORNER 24. PORTSMOUTH 45. RIPLEY 3. GUILDFORD 3.

25

158: Milestone at Effingham *Drawing by P Watkins*

165 SEND (2)
TQ 039 548   ✳
On A3 by Heron petrol station, Burnt Common. HYDE PARK CORNER 23.

166 SHALFORD (1)
TQ 000 465   ✳
On A 281 in front of Holbrook House, Horsham Lane. Apart from **BRIGHTON 40**, the inscription is almost unreadable now.

167 SHALFORD (2)
SU 999 481   ✳
On east side of Shalford Rd, 20 yards north of Tillingbourne Bridge. **HORSHAM 19**.

168 WEST CLANDON (1)
TQ 035 509   ✳
On A 246 near The Quarry. Although the stone reads **2m GUILDFORD, 9½m LEATHER-HEAD**, and **28 m LONDON**, it was discovered when it was exposed in 1976 and re-sited that it had been re-used; the original inscription read **3m LEATHERHEAD, 8m 3f GUILDFORD**.

169 WEST CLANDON. (2)
TQ 050 512   ✳
On A 246 between East and West Clandon. **LONDON 27, GUILDFORD 3, LEATHERHEAD 8½**.

170 WEST HORSLEY
TQ 079 523   ✳
On south side of A 246 opposite entrance to lay-by outside Cranmore School. **LONDON 25, GUILDFORD 5, LEATHERHEAD 6½**.

171 WISLEY
TQ 070 581   ✳
On A3 near Hyde Lane. **HYDE PARK CORNER 20**.

PROPERTY MARKERS

Stones which mark parliamentary boundaries and estates do not appear to have an industrial significance apart from the study of the spreading of a town as the population grew. For further information of Guildford's marker stones, see articles by Richard Williams in the Newsletters of the Surrey Archaeological Society's Guildford Group especially December 1988 and December 1989. Two markers of railway property mentioned in the December 1989 article are of interest, however. (See below). Since then a number of others have been found in the central Guildford area and at Peasmarsh.

172 GUILDFORD
TQ 991 495   ✳
Cast iron marker for the London and South Western Railway Company beside the railing on the north side of the rear station entrance in Guildford Park Road.

173 GUILDFORD
SU 992 493   ✳
Another marker from the L & S W R Co. beside a wall on the northern side of The Mount, just down hill from Wodeland Avenue.

174 ALBURY: OLD CHURCH DOOR
TQ 063 477   *

Strapwork on door of old Saxon church in Albury Park. The original village was moved away from here to its present position a mile away and five of the bells in the new church (TQ 050 476) are from the ancient church. Four of them were made by William Eldridge of Chertsey Foundry in 1695; the fifth bell dates from 1616.

175 EAST CLANDON: HATCHLANDS GATES
TQ 077 529   *

At end of Pincott lane. Gates to Hatchlands, former home of Admiral Vernon. The house dates from 1759. Less highly ornamented than the Onslows' at East Clandon (site 182) but with coat of arms (motto: *Labore et Consilio*) and heraldic motifs. No longer leading to the driveway up to the house.

176 GUILDFORD: HIGH STREET
SU 998 495   *

There are many pieces of work worth noticing, for example, the archway and the railings of Holy Trinity Church (1730s to 1880s), the archway of Abbott's Hospital and the decorative ironwork around the clock on balcony of the Guildhall. Also the balustrade by the entrance steps to Somerset House in Upper High Street.

177 GUILDFORD: QUARRY STREET
SU 998 492   *

Hill House in Quarry Street has an ancient door with elaborate wrought iron straps.

178 OCKHAM
TQ 057 569, 067 567 and 066 567   *

Ockham Park. Ornamental gates (about 1710) on Portsmouth Road and off Ockham Road. The Bridgefoot gates by the old A3 road allowed access to the Ripley side of the estate for goods vehicles to avoid Lambarts Hill. They were removed from their original position, re-erected across the front of Ockham Park House and now face towards Ockham Church. The Buckingham gates in Ockham Road south came from Buckingham House (later Palace); the lion statuettes on either side are reputed to have been used by Landseer as models for the Trafalgar Square lions. The present gates on Portsmouth Road are modern, of a fairly simple design and have rivals 100 yards to the south at Footbridge House.

179 PUTTENHAM: MONUMENT
SU 939 477   *

Cast iron posts, railings and flagstaff base on stone plinth commemorating the visit of Queen Victoria to Puttenham Heath in 1858 (Army Field Day). Base of flagstaff has inscription FILMER AND MASON, VICTORIA FOUNDRY, GUILDFORD, JUNE 1897. The original flagstaff was blown down. Site is on top of tumulus at edge of golf course.

180 PUTTENHAM: GATES
SU 932 477   *

Gates to Puttenham Priory. (See also 139)

181 SHERE: FOUNTAIN
TQ 074 479   *

Roadside drinking fountain with ironwork of Art Deco design. The Misses Spotteswood, looking on alcohol as the demon drink, commissioned J Brown of Albury Heath to bore a well here in 1886. Their initials form the centre of the bronze plaque above the well which is 280 feet deep. Water flowed here until the 1970s when Thames Water sank fresh boreholes, lowering the water table by 18", thus stopping the flow.

182 WEST CLANDON: CLANDON PARK GATES
TQ 031 508   LSII* *

See back cover photograph

Very ornate gates to Clandon Park, the home of the Onslow family. Made about 1776. Imposing situation but drive way no longer in use.

METAL GRAVE MARKERS

A speciality of several iron foundries in the 19th C. was the production of grave markers. These were often produced in large quantities for retailing cheaply; the Guildford firm of Filmer and Mason certainly produced several different types. (See article *Filmer and Mason, Guildford, Surrey* by Tony Yoward, SIHG Newsletter No. 64 for details.) There are a few to be found in churchyards in the Guildford area. Shere churchyard, (TQ 074478),

183: Iron grave marker, Stoke churchyard
Photo: Chris Shepheard

for example, has 4, three of which have no discernible identifications and one the faint remains of a painted dedication. St Mary's Church at Shackleford, has one example. One of the Filmer and Mason products can also be found in the churchyard at Tongham (**SU 887 489**). Ockham church (**TQ 066 565**) has one Filmer and Mason with undecipherable date and a simple iron surround, plus two other undated cast iron markers of a more ornate pattern made by the Etna foundry of Glasgow. Other grave markers made of metal and of interest are as follows.

183 GUILDFORD: STOKE CHURCH
SU 997 507   ✱

In 'new' Graveyard of Stoke Church, on the west side of Stoke Road. An unusual ornate cast iron graveslab made by D Goodyer of Guildford. In a half-roundel at the top, two Venuses and three Cupids with bows and arrows are shown commemorating Elizabeth Newington who died in 1875 when the slab was presumably cast. An inscription to her husband, David, was inserted in 1881 with a new fourline cast strip.

184 GUILDFORD: TRINITY CHURCHYARD
SU 998 495   ✱

Trinity Churchyard, High Street, has a First World War memorial to Major Geoffrey Parnell, of the 1st Battalion of the Queen's Regiment and to the men of that Battalion who fell at the Battle of the Somme in 1916. Made of bronze in the form of a winged angel bearing a sword, it was designed by his sister, Edith Farmiloe.

185 RIPLEY
TQ 051 566   ✱

The grave yard of Ripley parish church has the burial plot of the Law family of Ripley Court (1900-1927). Though badly overgrown, the four sides of the plot are marked out with unusual cast iron curbs decorated with acorns and oak leaves in an Art Deco style. Nearby, the grave of the Dibble girls (See article *Early Cycles & Cycling in the Guildford Area* by Les Bowerman, page 34) has engraved the memorial line:

I COULD GET SO FAR AND NO FARTHER

---

9   MISCELLANEOUS

---

186 GUILDFORD: HIGH STREET
SU 998 495   ✱

Mathematical tiles, end of rear gable wall of Guildford House, High St. This sort of 18th century surface decoration is also to be found on Parsons' Almshouse,(1796), Stoke Road, (**SU 998 502**) where high up on the end wall facing Onslow Rd. is an area of tiles 6ft x 20 ft.

187 GUILDFORD: MERROW
TQ 025 518   ✱

Model Cottages, Merrow Common. Designed by Clough Williams Ellis in 1913 to win a competition run by *The Spectator* magazine to find the best solution to the problem of a cheap housing system for low-paid agricultural workers. Made of timber for £100 each house.

After the First World War, Clough Williams Ellis designed for a worker from the Guildford brickworks who had been gassed badly in France a very cheap building whose walls could be made from rammed earth (*pise de terre*) but with brick chimneys and a pantiled roof. This was put up in about four weeks at Newlands Corner and is now known as the White Cottage (**TQ 044 493**). Brick cladding has recently been added.

Ellis also built for his own use at Stapledown, near Shere, a tree house around two Scots Fir trees, using timber and a corrugated iron roof.

188 SHALFORD: WAR DEFENCES
TQ 001 475   *

Near *The Sea Horse* public house. A plaque on the remains of a concrete road block commemorates the fact that this area was used as part of the 'GHQ Stop Line' defending London and the Home Counties during the Second World War. This was a series of pillboxes and other defences intended to halt the advance of Hitler's forces if they had landed. The Tillingbourne would have been utilised as an anti-tank ditch.

189 WANBOROUGH: FLAX POND
SU 934 502   ❐

Little Flexford. Large rectangular pond with level bottom for 'retting' flax (soaking flax plants with water till the soft outer tissue falls off to leave the fibres for making linen), together with sluices for controlling the water level. The owner of Little Flexford suggests that because of the Roman settlement at Wanborough, flax may have been grown there for linen making since those times. Documentary evidence for flax growing on this site has been found from 1309. A small historical exhibition is open to the public; flax and woad growing can also be seen there.

190 WEST HORSLEY: WEST HORSLEY PLACE
TQ 088 530   ❐

A Jacobean mansion originally 14th century but re-modelled in 1630s, including mathematical tiles on the west side to hide timber framing. It also has a rarity in Surrey–a crinkle-crankle or serpentine wall, an undulating brick wall designed to trap all available sunshine for fruit growing.

ADMIRALTY TELEGRAPH STATIONS

191 GUILDFORD: PEWLEY
TQ 002 492   LSII *

Semaphore station, Semaphore Road, Pewley Hill. One of the Admiralty signalling stations erected on high ground in 1821-22 between London and Portsmouth. The building was used for private accommodation from 1848 and a cupola was added in 1851.

A similar semaphore station, built as a tall tower, was situated where the Hog's Back

187 'Model cottage', Merrow *Photo: Chris Shepheard*

191: 'Semaphore House', Guildford
Photo: Chris Shepheard

29

Hotel is now (**SU 893 482**). This was part of the semaphore line from London to Plymouth which was never completed. Messages were relayed down from London to a junction station at Chatley Heath (see *A Guide to the Industrial Archaeology of the Elmbridge Borough area*) and thence to an octagonal tower (now destroyed) beside the church at Worplesdon (**SU 971 541**) and on to the Hog's Back, Binsted and Four Marks stations in Hampshire.

FORMER FIRE STATIONS

192 GUILDFORD: NORTH STREET
SU 997 496   ✳

The headquarters of the Guildford Fire Brigade service from 1872 to 1937 but now public lavatories.

193 GUILDFORD: WALNUT TREE CLOSE
SU 992 499   ✳

Caxton Works Fire Brigade, (Billings). Now occupied by Wepac Ltd. The Billings works brigade was certainly in existence in 1913, starting life with a manual pump, later using a steam pump from Guildford Borough whom it assisted when called on for help at large fires. Believed to have been stood down after World War Two. During the War (1939-45), both the Sports Pavilion, Woodbridge Road, Guildford and the Yellow Bus Garage in Worplesdon Road, Guildford were also used as fire stations.

194 RIPLEY: ROSE LANE
TQ 053 567   ✳

A brick building, recently re-fronted, with a small belfry and a terracotta plaque dated 1911. Closed as a Fire Station in 1960; now used by the local Scouts. Its predecessor is in Newark Lane near Vine Cottages, (**TQ 051 568**) a small

30

194 Former fire sation, Ripley *Photo: Chris Shepheard*

brick building with double doors, probably used by the Ripley Volunteer Brigade from 1891 to 1910. This building may have housed the local parish pump before 1800 and had protected the country house estate of Hatchlands. Originally it was the mortuary for the almshouses adjoining which were built in 1738, the end part of which was destroyed by a bomb in World War II.

195 SHERE: MIDDLE STREET
TQ 073 478   ✳

Has a gabled roof with conical belfry. The Shere and Albury Fire Volunteer Fire Brigade was formed in 1883 and the fire station was built in 1885. The Brigade was probably stood down in 1917. Converted into public lavatories in 1977.

196 CHILWORTH: NEW ROAD
TQ 030 473   ✳

Created in 1938 for the Auxiliary Fire Service and housed in the garage of the Tillingbourne Bus Company. In 1948 the station became part of the Surrey Fire Brigade and a new fire station was built in the grounds of the School in New Road whilst the original station returned to use by the Bus Company.

MEDIEVAL SHOP PREMISES

At least two medieval shop premises still exist in Guildford High Street. They survive as undercrofts or basements with a ceiling above street level leaving room for a doorway and steps and often a spiral stair to the merchant's shop above. The finest example is at 72-78 High Street (**SU 997 494**) beneath the Halifax Building Society, used by the Guildford Tourist Information Centre, and is now scheduled as an Ancient Monument. It measures about 30 feet by 19 and probably was constructed in the 13th C. The arched stone vaulting of the roof is supported by two central pillars, the ribs being supported around the walls by brackets called corbels which are carved in the shape of faces, some of them human, others as grotesque creatures. Another similar undercroft lies below the *Angel Hotel* just across the road. It is now used as a restaurant.

COMMERCIAL AND RETAIL FIRMS OF LONG STANDING

197 GUILDFORD
SU 998 497   ✳

Biddles, (now Straker Biddles), Ward Street. Formerly printers and binders, now stationers. 1885.

198 GUILDFORD
TQ 001 525 ✳
Bowden and Higlett, Slyfield Green Industrial Estate. Started about 1895 by installing generating sets in the large local houses and they also did much of the wiring-up of Guildford. Later they became motor vehicle electrical parts suppliers.

199 GUILDFORD
SU 998 494 ✳
Frost Bros., 14 Tunsgate. Chartered Surveyors. 1862.

200 GUILDFORD
SU 996 494 ✳
Gwinn, 3 Chapel Street. A grocer's shop which recently closed after 154 year old history. One of the oldest family businesses in the area, it sold bread and meal, and was a bakery for the people of Guildford. It has been sold complete with its bread oven and flour loft but the old meal bins and wooden cash desk were rescued for Guildford Museum.

201 GUILDFORD
SU 999 497 ✳
Hampton & Sons, 8 Chertsey St. Estate agents. 1830.

202 GUILDFORD
TQ 001 496 ✳
Heath & Salter, 254 High St. Estate agents. 1889.

203 GUILDFORD
SU 998 494 ✳
Jeffery's, High St. Famous for sporting equipment since it was started in 1851 by Richard Jeffery, a gunmaker.

204 GUILDFORD
SU 999 496 ✳
Messingers for Tools, Chertsey St. Suppliers of hand or powered tools since 1906.

205 GUILDFORD
SU 992 506 ✳
John Moon and Co, 1848. Timber merchants, first at St Mary's Wharf and from 1935 in Walnut Tree Close. Now part of Sabah Timber.

206 GUILDFORD
SU 995 496 ✳
Moffat & Co, 2 Woodbridge Road. Men's outfitters. 1927.

207 GUILDFORD
SU 993 499 ✳
Pimms Funeral Services, Mary Road. A family business since 1835 but in 1979 taken over by F A Holland & Son (dating from 1850).

208 GUILDFORD
SU 996 494 ✳
Read and Co, Chapel St. Butchers since 1750. Guildford's oldest family owned business.

209 GUILDFORD
SU 997 494 ✳
Salsbury & Sons Ltd, High Street. Jewellers and silversmiths started in 1870, having taken over from a firm of watchmakers there since the 1840s.

210 GUILDFORD
SU 996 494 ✳
Weller Eggar, 4 Quarry St. Estate agents. 1871

211 GUILDFORD
SU 992 505 ✳
Williams Bros, Woodbridge Meadows. Wholesale and retail sellers of newspapers and magazines since 1908.

212 GUILDFORD
SU 934 528 ■
Vokes Ltd: Normandy. Internationally known makers of oil and air filters for engineering purposes. Formed by Cecil Gordon Vokes in 1921. When their original Putney premises were bombed out in 1940, the company moved to Henley Park, home of Lord Pirbright. The firm became part of BTR plc in 1983.

213 GUILDFORD
SU 988 505 ✳
Weyside · Engineering, Midleton Industrial Estate. Started in 1926 as a small motor repair firm in Madrid Road, Guildford, which even made a few electric cars in the 1950s but is now a major manufacturer of aircraft and precision components particularly for the Tornado and Harrier aircraft.

214 EAST HORSLEY
TQ 092 544 ✳
A H Conisbee, 15 Station Parade. Butchers since before 1861. Also at 207 Epsom Road, Merrow, Guildford.

215 RIPLEY
TQ 052 567 ✳
Methold Engineering Ltd, Portsmouth Road. A garage since 1927.

216 RIPLEY: NEWARK LANE
TQ 051 568 ✳
Stansfield Bros Ltd. Were mineral water manufacturers from 1840, adjoining a former inn called *The George*, but their buildings have been sold to a brewery and now are used only for distribution.

In addition it should be noted that the huge, nationally known firm, **Unigate**, was started in 1750 in a small grocer's shop owned by Charles Gates in Guildford High Street next to the **Three Pigeons Inn**. His sons joined the Salvation Army during the later 19th century, publicly poured the wines and spirits down the drain, and changed to the sale of dairy products. The Cow and Gate trademark was registered in 1891. In 1959 they amalgamated with United Dairies to form Unigate Ltd.

ENTERTAINMENT INDUSTRY

217 GUILDFORD:
UPPER HIGH STREET
SU 999 495   ✱

Thorp's Bookshop, formerly the Constitutional Hall, was Guildford's first picture house. West's Picture Palace had a special installation of electric lights laid on by the Guildford Electricity Supply Company in 1909 but in 1910 it was refused a licence because of the inflammable nature of the building.

218 GUILDFORD: ONSLOW STREET
SU 994 496   ✱

Harper's. As the Central Hall Picture Palace, this was the first purpose-built cinema, accommodating 700 people. It has had several changes of name. From 1930 it was The Plaza but in 1956 it closed as a cinema and became the Plaza Ballroom, changing in due course to the Coral Bingo Hall which closed down in July 1991 but re-opened in 1992 as a night club.

219 GUILDFORD:
STUDIO ONE CINEMA
SU 995 496   ✱

Woodbridge Road. Again several changes of name and usage. It started as the Pelham House Roller Skating Rink in 1911 but changed to The Pelham Concert Hall for a short while, swiftly re-opening as The Guildford Cinema in December 1911. In 1959 it became the Astor and changed again to Studio 1 in March 1970. In May 1970 the balcony was used for Studio 2. When the Cannon Company took over in 1985, it became Cannon 1 and 2. The Cannon closed down in March 1988 but then re-opened as Flicks night club in 1990.

220 GUILDFORD: ODEON CINEMA
TQ 002 497   ✱

Epsom Road. Opened in 1935; designed by Andrew Mather, originally with 1800 seats. Of note are the four bas-relief panels of stone on the facade. The cinema was tripled in 1971 and a fourth screen was added in 1988.

PEOPLE

William of Ockham (1285-1348 approx) Franciscan friar and philosopher. Published but probably did not originate, the principle that entities are not to be multiplied without necessity. This, known as Occam's Razor and interpreted as the need always to accept the simplest interpretation of the facts available, has always been a tenet of scientific theory. A small painted window in the Ockham parish church commemorates its most famous local son, the 'Doctor Invincibilis'.

Richard Oastler (1789-1861) was a pioneer in social history related to the Industrial Revolution who lived the last years of his life in South Hill Cottage, overlooking Guildford Castle. In the north of England he made untiring efforts to improve the lot of the workers, striving to awaken the conscience of the employers by advocating a working day limited to ten hours, opposing the vicious Poor Laws and Factory Laws and teaching the oppressed to fight their own battles. Thousands of people attended his funeral, and 100,000 attended the unveiling of a statue to him in Bradford eight years later.

William King (1805-1893), Baron King of Ockham, First Earl of Lovelace. Amateur civil engineer whose publications include an account of the bent wood laminated truss roof of the hall at his house, Horsley Towers. He built extensively in and around Horsley in a distinctive style, using flint and brick.

William Le Queux, a pioneer wireless enthusiast, made his home in Guildford for a short time. He lived at West Mount from 1919 to 1922. His call sign was 2AZ. He was better known as a writer of popular detective fiction like Sir Arthur Conan Doyle. His stories, however, often brought in the wonders of wireless waves.

T O M Sopwith, aircraft engineer, lived at Horsley Towers, East Horsley, during the early part of this century.

Plaque on the house of computer pioneer Alan Turing, in Guildford   *Photo: Chris Shepheard*

Sir Barnes Wallis who joined Vickers at Brooklands in 1930, lived in Effingham and died in 1979. He pioneered geodetic structures in airships and in the Wellington bomber as well as producing such well-known inventions as the 'Bouncing Bomb', and the Swing-Wing Aircraft. He advanced revolutionary ideas such as the hypersonic aircraft and the cargo carrying submarine.

Remarkably, the Guildford area has associations with several key people in the world of mathematics and its applications, especially computing.

William Oughtred (died 1660) was vicar of Shalford in 1603 and of Albury in 1610. His first book, 'Key of Mathematics' (1631) influenced Newton 30 years later. It summarises arithmetic and algebra which in those days were difficult to understand. Recognising the need for standard symbols to identify mathematical quantities and operations, he invented 150 symbols, though only the multiplication sign is universally known today. Quick to see the practical applications of Napier's logarithms, Oughtred invented the slide rule in 1622. In this early form of computer, two logarithmic scales move side by side, providing a quick and simple means of adding two logarithms and therefore of multiplying the corresponding numbers.

Thomas Malthus, (1666-1734), who lived in Albury, wrote his famous 'Essay on Population' and stimulated many modern studies in economics as well as influencing Charles Darwin towards his theory of evolution by natural selection. Darwin was also a frequent visitor to Albury.

John Rickman was a pupil of the Guildford Grammar School who spent 38 years in the House of Commons, 12 as Speaker's Secretary and 26 as Clerk Assistant at the Table. His claim to arithmetical fame is that he instigated and organised the first census of population in 1801.

Ada Lovelace, (1815-1852), daughter of the poet Lord Byron and first wife of the Earl of Lovelace who left his mark on the architecture of East Horsley, possessed considerable mathematical ability, and helped Charles Babbage in his unfulfilled task of producing the Difference and Analytical Engines. The importance of her contribution to Babbage's work is not clear but she was certainly closely involved with it and translated and commented on an Italian account of the engines. The suggestion that she wrote computer programs is recorded by the programming language ADA named after her.

'Lewis Carroll', whose real name was the Rev. Charles Luttwidge Dodgson, was a mathematics lecturer at Oxford from 1855 to 1881 frequently visiting his sisters from 1868 to 1898 at 'The Chestnuts', Castle Hill, Guildford, where he died and was buried in The Mount cemetery, Guildford. His book 'Symbolic Logic' is described as one of the most brilliant logic textbooks ever written. The 'Alice' stories, although written for children's entertainment, frequently make fun of problems in logic.

Alan Turing. A plaque on number 22 Ennismore Avenue, Guildford, records that the house was 'The family home of Alan M Turing, 1912-1954, Founder of Computer Science'. Turing was a brilliant, if eccentric, mathematician who carried out pioneering work on the theory of computing in the 1930's. During the Second World War he was involved with the construction and use of computers for cryptography. Later he worked at the National Physical Laboratory at Teddington and at Manchester University.

by Les Bowerman

Baron Karl von Drais of Karlsruhe in 1817 was the first to produce a rideable bicycle, the draisienne or hobby-horse, which was propelled by striking the feet on the ground. It had a brief craze in England but was not accepted as a practical vehicle. Four-wheeled velocipedes with treadles, a cranked rear axle and tiller front steering had a similarly brief life in the 1850's but were too heavy. Pierre Michaux, a Parisian coachmaker made the breakthrough when he attached pedals to cranks on the front axle of a draisienne, and in 1861 produced the first pedal-cycle for sale. Such machines soon became popular in this country, but the *Surrey*

Comet in 1869 doubted whether this 'machine of solitary locomotion' would ever replace the horse. Nevertheless the possibilities of balancing indefinitely on two wheels whilst propelling oneself at more than running speed were quickly realised.

By 1870 'Excelsior' two wheel velocipedes, or boneshakers as they soon became known (more from the sound the iron tyres made on untarred roads than because of any innate discomfort) made by Gray & Co., of London were being sold by J Hooke of 80 High St. Guildford as advertised in Hooke's Almanack. Guildford Museum has a similar machine and

Advert for the Ripley tricycle

The RIPLEY TRICYCLE for 1888 is equally suitable for LADY or GENTLEMAN

Reproduced by courtesy of Les Bowerman

ARRIVING AT THE ANCHOR AT RIPLEY.

The Anchor, Ripley

Reproduced by courtesy of Les Bowerman

sells a photograph taken originally by Lewis Carroll of his brother Wilfred astride one outside 'The Chestnuts', the family home in Guildford.

One of the first in Surrey to adopt the new vehicle was John Keen of Surbiton who perhaps more than anybody else developed the unwieldy wooden-wheeled boneshaker into the elegant old high Ordinary bicycle with iron rim and wire tension spokes. Apart from Keen and a few manufacturers in the Croydon area, very little cycle industry was generated in Surrey at this stage, all of the activity being on the social side. This was probably because the middle-class sporting cyclists from the Metropolis found Surrey a natural playground. To be effective, the developing bicycle needed a none too hilly road with a good surface, and the Guildford road, turnpiked from 1749 but largely deserted since the railway reached Portsmouth in 1847, was ideal. Keen, an artisan and one who raced for money, had to be a professional, but he encouraged the gentlemen amateurs who quickly formed themselves into clubs.

One of the earliest clubs was the Surrey Bicycle Club in 1871, and in August 1876 'this tip-top racing club' held their captaincy race from the *Griffin* at Kingston to Guildford and back to Ripley, a distance of 24 miles. H Osborne won in just over 16mph. Compare this with Kilvert's 1871 statement that 'when the Queen comes over from Windsor to Clare-

mont she drives at a great pace, 12 miles an hour'. The Guildford BC was formed in 1877. Could the fleeting visit of the Surrey the previous year have been the spur? Ripley was already clearly a favourite venue, and in 1881 it was written 'to no place in the whole island of Great Britain do more bicyclists wend their way than to the quiet and pretty Surrey village of Ripley'. The *Talbot* was then the favoured stop for 'sober-minded cyclists' while 'youths of great vitality' made things lively at the *Anchor*, and there was 'rare merrymaking' at the *Hautboy and Fiddle*.

During the 1880's the *Anchor* with its old-world charm and the kindly ministrations of Harriet Dibble and her two daughters, Annie and Harriet, became so famous that cyclists came from all over the world as the Cyclists Visitors Books, still kept at the *Anchor*, prove. The 1884 book has 5,896 signatures. Police exaggeratedly claimed that 20,000 cyclists passed through Kingston en route for Ripley on Whit Sunday 1894. When the two daughters died in 1895 and 1896, their cyclist customers subscribed for the stained glass window and brass plaque to their memory in Ripley church. One of the window glass panels was stolen in May 1991.

In July 1883, the London Tricycle Club organised a 24 hour race starting at Caterham and finishing in the Ripley area. 67 tricyclists started at midnight. By 9.30 pm John Keen, assisting on his Ordinary, dashed into Ripley and ordered tea; 9 minutes later T R Marriott, the first of the competitors, arrived, had a mouthful of tea and pushed on to win at Merton with 218 3/4 miles, a record. Marriott was in partnership with Thomas Humber and Fred Cooper and the win obviously helped business enormously. A lightweight racing tricycle called the 'Ripley' was marketed by Marriott & Cooper afterwards, albeit made by Rudge at Coventry. The name of the otherwise obscure rural Surrey village was also used by A W Gamage Ltd. for the 'Ripley' road cycling shoe which was on sale for at least a quarter of a century.

1885 was the year when John Kemp Starley 'set the fashion to the world' with his Rover safety bicycle, the basic layout of which is still used today as the standard diamond-frame. Its success led to an upsurge in cycling and many new clubs. The North Road Cycling Club was the first designed to bring together for social and competitive riding the best riders from a wide area, and the Ripley Road Club for the 'best Metropolitan men' was the second early in 1886. Their favourite run was the Ripley Road, especially from the *Angel* at Thames Ditton to the *Anchor* at Ripley, and their member, Dr E B Turner, FRCS, presented a magnificent shield to be competed for over this course. It was won by A L Bower who in 1924 became Lord Mayor of London. The trophy is now the 'President's Shield' of the Veteran-Cycle Club who in 1986 celebrated its centenary with a ride over the course on old machines. Unfortunately the Ripley RC faded after about 4 years but was superseded by the Bath Road Club who did most of their social riding on the Ripley Road. In the 1890's the Bath Road Club instituted a series of dinners for the roadmenders, held in turn at inns along the road, including of course the *Anchor* at Ripley.

1886 also saw the first of the Southern Counties Cyclists Camps at Shalford Park, Guildford. There were 125 campers in 60 bell tents equipped with four hammocks apiece, plus reception, concert and dining marquees. The Guildford CC (as it had by then been re-named) won a competition for the best-decorated reception tent—they had lace and crimson drapery, plush-covered furniture, mahogany sideboard with musical box, and piano 'prettily embowered' with flowers and foliage, the entrance being guarded by two brass cannons under the Guildford arms. Racing was at the original cricket ground in Woodbridge Road, watched by a gate of between three and four thousand.

The main event was the one mile handicap open to ordinary ie high, bicycles, safety bicycles and tricycles for the Anchor Challenge Shield presented for the occasion by Mrs Harriet Dibble. It was won fittingly by Harold Crooke of the Guildford club on a 'Rapid' roadster Ordinary. The Veteran-Cycle Club celebrated the centenary over the equivalent week in 1986 with 75 in camp at Farncombe and the Shield on display, as featured in the *Surrey Advertiser*. A most remarkable cycle was ridden around the Guildford area in 1887. It consisted of five high-wheeled Singer tandem tricycles coupled together. Because of the interest shown by the War Office, it was called the Victoria War-Cycle. Ten riders collected it from the showrooms at Holborn Viaduct, rode it down to Ripley to be ministered to by Annie Dibble, and over the Hog's Back to Aldershot. After demonstrating it to the military next morning, they rode it back to Guildford with 300 lbs of luggage, and up the High Street where 'carters and other travellers got out of our way very quickly indeed', to Ripley again where 'the entire population' turned out and habitues of the *Anchor* remarked that 'Ripley Fair isn't in it'. Then back again over Stringers Common to Aldershot.

The success of the rear-driven safety and the re-invention of the pneumatic tyre by John Boyd Dunlop in 1888 meant that cycling became more practical for women, and the bicycle a principal factor in their emancipation. The Rational Dress Association sought to make long, baggy knickerbockers acceptable in place of the then ground-length skirts and petticoats. One of the leaders was Lady Florence Harberton. In 1898 rationally dressed she called at the *Hautboy* at Ockham for refreshment. 'Not in the coffee room in that dress', she was told by Mrs Sprague, the innkeeper. The latter was prosecuted at Kingston Quarter Sessions the following year for refusing refreshment to a traveller. She was acquitted but the case established that an innkeeper could not refuse refreshment to wearers of rational dress, albeit that the customer could not demand service in a particular room; Mrs Sprague had directed the noble lady to the bar parlour which the latter claimed 'smelled abominable' and in which there may have been working men without their coats.

In 1895 John and Raymond Dennis opened a cycle shop at the foot of Guildford High Street. They also used the Volunteer drill hall as a riding school. Rapidly expanding, they soon advertised themselves as the largest cycle manufacturers in south-east England. In 1899 John was fined for travelling up the High Street on a motorcycle at an alleged speed of 16mph–believed by the cycling journals to be impossible but used by the astute Dennis in advertisements to prove the speed of his machines. By 1905 the motor side was so successful that they discontinued bicycles. Only two Dennis Bros. bicycles are known to have survived, one of which, owned by John Dennis, grandson of the founder, may be seen at Guildford Museum.

The Guildford CC lasted for 46 years until the Great War. It had an early rival in the form of the Guildford Castle BC, but by the turn of the century the club must have seemed too old and staid to appeal to younger riders, as a result of which the Stoke CC, the Guildford Wheelers CC and in 1903 the Charlotteville CC were formed. Only the last survived the Great War.

Between wars, the Charlotteville rose from a small provincial club into a nationally famous one. It has a long and proud history but that is another story. Suffice to say that it re-introduced massed start road-racing to this country at Brooklands in 1933, has produced several national record-holders, and was famous far beyond Guildford for its Whit Monday Sports meetings at Woodbridge Road. It is still going strong and welcomes prospective members to its Friday evening meetings at the Waterside Centre, Guildford. This writer has been a member for more than 40 years.

CHILWORTH GUNPOWDER MILLS

by Glenys Crocker

Surrey played an important role in the gunpowder industry in Britain, particularly in its early stages. Some 18 manufacturing sites of various dates are known in the county. The earliest were at Rotherhithe in the mid-16th century and these were followed by mills at Tolworth, Godstone, Wotton and Abinger, a few kilometres up the Tillingbourne valley from Chilworth. The Chilworth mills were established by the East India Company in 1626. They were the longest running mills in the county, continuing until 1920. Many mills closed at this time in the rationalisation of the explosives industry which followed the end of the First World War.

The Chilworth mills were expanded in the late 17th century to supply government contracts and occupied a stretch of the valley up to Postford Pond. The mills at Postford then became derelict. Eventually paper mills were built on the site in the 19th century, followed by a flock mill and by Bottings' corn mill (site 50). The lower powder mills, to the west of Blacksmith Lane, were converted to paper mills in 1704. These were followed by Unwins printing works from 1871 to 1895 when the factory burned down and the firm moved to

West Lodge entrance to Chilworth gunpowder mills   *Photo: Chris Shepheard*   **37**

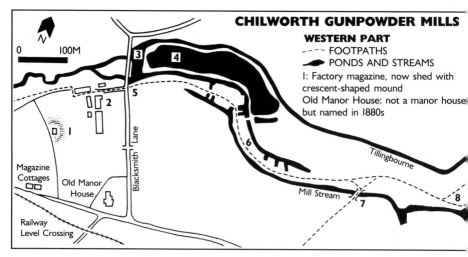

CHILWORTH GUNPOWDER MILLS

WESTERN PART

---- FOOTPATHS
◣ PONDS AND STREAMS

1: Factory magazine, now shed with
crescent-shaped mound
Old Manor House: not a manor house
but named in 1880s

0   100M

Magazine
Cottages
Old Manor
House
Blacksmith Lane
Tillingbourne
Mill Stream
Railway
Level Crossing

Old Woking. The powder mills expanded up the valley again in the 19th century, particularly after the introduction of new technology from 1885 onwards.

Gunpowder is a mixture of saltpetre, charcoal and sulphur, generally in the proportions 75:15:10. The prepared ingredients were moistened and 'incorporated' by being crushed and ground together under heavy edge-runner stones for several hours. The resulting mill-cake was then pressed, granulated or 'corned', glazed, dusted, dried and packed in barrels for distribution. Because several water-powered processes were involved, gunpowder sites typically have complex water courses. They also have ample tree cover to absorb the blast from any explosions and well-spaced buildings to reduce the risk of multiple accidents Remains are usually ruinous, as at Chilworth.

A footpath from East Shalford leads to the wes end of the site, passing a private garden which contains the large mound of the factory magazine (1). Several materials processing anc servicing buildings (2) have been re-used by modern businesses. The nearby 'Old Cottage and 'Rose Cottage' were converted from the drying lofts of a paper mill. Blacksmith Lane runs along the mill dam of the original works. The mill dam (3) is a small rectangular feature fed by two streams and the larger pond (4) was constructed in the 1980s for fishing. The next part of the site is entered by a gate at the former entrance lodge (5).

From here to the Lockner Farm lane, the land

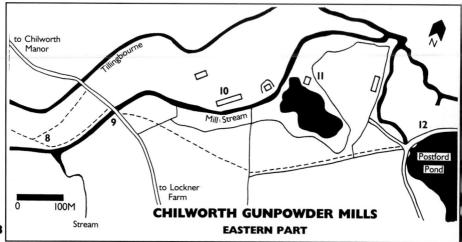

to Chilworth
Manor

Tillingbourne

Mill Stream

to Lockner
Farm

0   100M

Stream

Postford
Pond

CHILWORTH GUNPOWDER MILLS

EASTERN PART

is owned by Guildford Borough Council who permit access by a path running parallel to the millstream. This crosses several secondary mill leats which served individual process buildings. Several edge runner stones can be seen on the ground and some have been erected by the side of the path. (6) Behind them are the remains of a steam powered incorporating mill, including a circular bedstone, on which a pair of edge runners turned, and a steam engine bed. The works had an extensive hand-operated tramway system by the late 19th century, with a branch to Chilworth Station which is now a footpath. Punts were also used for transport and where the tramway crossed the millstream (7) there is a swingbridge, half timber and half iron, which allowed their passage. Further on, the path goes through the remains of a protective mound made of corrugated iron and earth (8) and then passes a row of six massive incorporating mill buildings of the 1880s. These had a typical structure consisting of strong walls at the back and sides

and a flimsy roof, traces of which remain. There are also traces of matchboarding on the internal walls and there are levers for a system of drenching the mills in the event of an explosion. From the lane (9) a public footpath continues east through fields. This affords a view of some of the buildings of the 1890s 'smokeless powder' factory which was built to manufacture modern nitrate explosives such as cordite. The buildings, which are on private land on the north bank of the river, include a brick hydraulic press house with several compartments including tall sections for the accumulators (10). The footpath continues across the site of the Admiralty cordite factory built in the First World War. This is represented by a stove (11) beside a pond formed in the 1980s and by many foundations. Botting's mill (12) (site 50) closed as an animal feed mill in 1991 and its site is being re-developed. The wood behind is called Colliers Hanger, after the colliers or charcoal burners who supplied charcoal for the powder mills.

Chilworth gunpowder mills; rear of 1880s mixing house and incorporating mills   *Photo: Chris Shepheard*

36: Fire engine made by Dennis Bros. 1920s

Alan Ingram Collection

FURTHER READING

S Beamon & S Roaf	*The Ice-Houses of Britain*. Routledge, 1990
J M Clarke	*The Brookwood Necropolis Railway*. Oakwood Press 1983/8
S Corke	*Guildford, a pictorial history*. Phillimore 1990
G Crocker	*A Guide to the Chilworth Gunpowder Mills*. SIHG 1990
G Crocker	*Chilworth Gunpowder*. SIHG 1984
J Janaway & R Head	*Guildford Past and Present*. Countryside Books 1985
S Jenkinson	*Ash and Ash Vale, a pictorial history*. Phillimore 1990
H E Malden	*A history of Surrey*. 1900.
L Oppitz	*Surrey Railways Remembered*. Countryside Books 1988
D Renn	*The River Wey Bridges between Farnham and Guildford*. Research Volume No 1 of the Surrey Archaeological Society
D Stidder	*The Watermills of Surrey*. Barracuda Books 1990

OTHER PUBLICATIONS OF THE SURREY INDUSTRIAL HISTORY GROUP

R G M Baker	*A Guide to the Industrial Archaeology of the Borough of Elmbridge*. 1990
G Crocker (editor)	*A Guide to the Industrial Archaeology of Surrey*. Prepared by SIHG and published by the Association for Industrial Archaeology. 1990
F Haveron	*A Guide to the Industrial Archaeology of the Waverley area*. 1985
J Mills	*A guide to the Industrial History of Runnymede*. 1991
C Shepheard (compiler)	*Surrey at work in old photographs*. Prepared by SIHG and published by Alan Sutton 1992
D Stidder	*The Industrial Archaeology of Reigate & Banstead District*.1979.